THE
POWER OF SYMPATHY

William Hill Brown

THE
POWER
OF SYMPATHY

Edited by William S. Kable

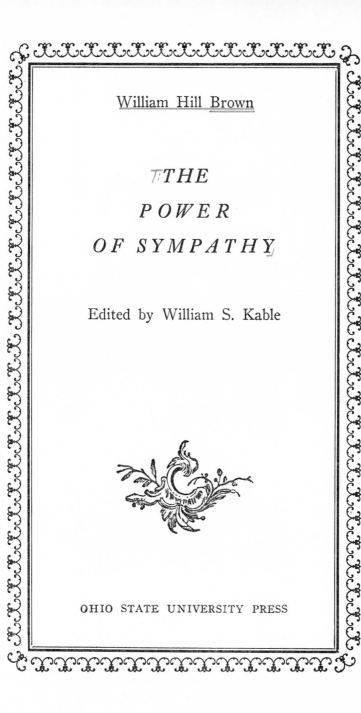

OHIO STATE UNIVERSITY PRESS

ACKNOWLEDGMENTS

To the following librarians and libraries, I should like to express my gratitude for assistance in the preparation of this edition: Mr. William H. Runge, whose hospitality always adds to a visit to the University of Virginia's Alderman Library; Mr. Richard Colles Johnson of The Newberry Library; the American Antiquarian Society; the Henry E. Huntington Library; the New York Public Library; and the Library of Congress.

The following research assistants at the University of South Carolina shared with me in good humor long hours of collation and proofreading: Dominick Hart, Patricia and Noel Polk, Miriam and Peter Shillingsburg.

William Hill Brown dedicated the first American novel "To the Young Ladies of United Columbia." I should like to dedicate my editorial labors on this edition of Brown's work to my friend John S. Van E. Kohn, who first introduced me to the glories of early American fiction.

William S. Kable

July 1, 1969

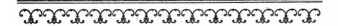

TABLE OF CONTENTS

ILLUSTRATIONS

Editor's Introduction

EDITOR'S INTRODUCTION

T HE Power of Sympathy is generally accepted as the first American novel, yet its right to that title could be, and has been, the subject for dispute. As in many arguments over such distinctions, the validity of the title depends on the definition of its terms. The first novel by a native of the territory now comprising the United States is *The Life of Harriot Stuart* (London: J. Payne and J. Bouquet, 1751), by Charlotte Ramsay Lennox.[1] Born in 1720, somewhere in New York State, possibly in Albany, Charlotte was the daughter of James Ramsay, a British army officer. After spending her childhood in America, she was sent to England in 1735, never to return to her native land. Her literary career produced a number of novels and translations which add little to

[1] For biographical data, see M. R. Small, *Charlotte Ramsay Lennox: An Eighteenth-Century Lady of Letters* (New Haven, Conn., 1935). The *DNB* and *DAB* articles are convenient summaries, although the latter misdates *Harriot Stuart* as 1750.

eighteenth-century letters, and she is best remembered for her friendship with Samuel Johnson, who gave an all-night party in honor of
the publication of her first novel, *The Life of
Harriot Stuart*. This two-volume novel contains autobiographical elements, some of which
describe what must be the author's youthful ex-
periences in America. Otherwise, the novel is
nothing more than a conventional combination
of the ingredients of sentimental romance and
the novel of manners, and it can be called American only by the accident of its author's birth.

Robert H. Elias has proposed a candidate for
the title of "first novel written by an American
citizen" in *Adventures of Alonso: Containing
Some Striking Anecdotes of the Present Prime
Minister of Portugal* (London: John Bew,
1775).[2] If Elias's attribution of this work to
Thomas Atwood Digges, a native of Warburton
Manor, Maryland, and a friend of no less an
American than George Washington, can be accepted, *Adventures of Alonso* can also be called
American by accident of its author's birth. But
the place of its composition and publication are
not American, and, more important, the novel

---

[2] Robert H. Elias, "The First American Novel," *American
Literature* XII (1940–41), 419–34.

itself does not contain American elements. Even the title-page designation, "By a Native of *Maryland,* some years resident in Lisbon," seems to have been reserved for promoting the sale of a later issue of the work in this country.

Lyle H. Wright's *American Fiction 1774-1850* contains three entries which antedate *The Power of Sympathy* (1789), but none of the three can be a candidate, strictly speaking, for the title of first American novel.[3] Francis Hopkinson's *A Pretty Story: Written in the Year of Our Lord 2774* (Philadelphia: John Dunlap and Williamsburg: John Pinkney, 1774) is a very short allegorical history of the relations between Great Britain and the American colonies down to the appointment of General Gage as colonial governor of Massachusetts. The pseudonymous *The Golden Age; or, Future Glory of North America by an Angel to Celadon, in Several Entertaining Visions* (n.p., 1785) is another slight political allegory, only sixteen pages long. The title alone of Peter Markoe's *The Algerine Spy in Pennsylvania; or, Letters Written by a Native of Algiers on the Affairs of the United States in America,*

---

[3] Lyle H. Wright, *American Fiction 1774–1850: A Contribution toward a Bibliography* (San Marino, Calif., 1948), p. 311.

from the Close of the Year 1783 to the Meeting of the Convention (Philadelphia: Prichard & Hall, 1787) betrays the work's closer kinship to political tract than novel.

The Power of Sympathy remains the most likely candidate for the honor of being called the first American novel. It is certainly a novel, that is, a sustained fictional narrative in prose. The two volumes in which it originally appeared amount to almost three hundred pages. Further, although there are sources in actual events for certain elements of the plot, and although the title page displays the oft-repeated claim "Founded in Truth," the work is presented as fiction. Finally the narrative is carried on by means of the epistolary technique, a highly conventional eighteenth-century device for presenting fictional narrative. One thing is certain: in his Preface the author defends the work specifically against the charges leveled at novels and makes it clear that the author's intention was that the work be considered a novel. And the novel is thoroughly American. The plot is set in New York, Rhode Island, and Boston; the fictional world of the book is consistently that of the young Republic. The work was also unquestionably written and published in the United States. *The Power of Sympathy*, therefore, deserves the distinction, first claimed for it in contemporary advertisements,[4] of being the first American novel.

II

The first edition of *The Power of Sympathy* is anonymous. The only detail it contains which can be construed as in any way providing information about the author is the first line of the verse on the title page, "Fain would he strew Life's thorny Way with Flowers. . . . " There is a possibility, however slight it may be, that the masculine pronoun of this line, if taken literally, points to a male author of the book. But there is no stronger piece of evidence concerning the authorship within the book itself. Nor was there any contemporary witness who named the author in print.

In the course of the nineteenth century, however, a persistent tradition grew up that Mrs. Sarah Wentworth Apthorp Morton,[5] a minor poet better known by her pseudonym, Philenia,

[4] See the "Bibliographical Note" by Milton Ellis, prefixed to the Facsimile Text Society reproduction of *The Power of Sympathy* (New York, 1937).

[5] The standard biography is by Emily Pendleton and Milton Ellis, *Philenia: The Life and Works of Sarah Wentworth Morton, 1759–1846* (Orono, Maine: Printed at the University Press, 1931).

was the author of the novel. The origin of this tradition is obscure, but it is apparently connected with the notorious Ophelia episode, which is contained in Letters XXI–XXIII of the novel and provides the subject for the engraved frontispiece. This episode recounts the tragic story of the seduction and consequent suicide of Fanny Apthorp, Mrs. Morton's sister; only the names are changed to throw a very thin veil of fiction over the widely rumored actual scandal. In the story, Ophelia (Frances Theodora Apthorp) is seduced by her sister's husband, Martin (Perez Morton). After their illicit relationship produces a child, Ophelia's father, Shepherd (Charles Apthorp) is bound and determined to bring about a settlement. Just before a scheduled confrontation of the various parties, Ophelia (Fanny) poisons herself. The frontispiece depicts the scene as Mr. and Mrs. Shepherd discover their dying daughter, who gasps, "O Fatal! Fatal Poison!"

Perhaps the association in the popular mind of the Morton scandal with the novel gave rise to the attribution of the book to Mrs. Morton, even though she would have been the last person to want to publicize a family scandal. The earliest written record of this attribution is in a manuscript note by Samuel Jennison made sometime in the middle of the century.[6] The earliest appearance of the attribution in print is in 1878: "The seduction of a near and dear relative is said to have formed the ground work of the first American novel, *The Power of Sympathy*, written by Mrs. Morton in 1787."[7] It is noteworthy that this statement misrepresents the importance of the Ophelia episode to the novel and also errs in its date.

In 1894 a Boston publisher issued a bulky edition of the novel, designed to appeal to the antiquarian interests of prospective purchasers. In his introduction, dated June 19, 1894, to this edition, Walter Littlefield attributes the work to Mrs. Morton, and the title page reads: "By Mrs. Perez Morton (Sarah Wentworth Apthorp)." A second reprint of the novel, in installments, began in the October, 1894, issue of the *Bostonian*. Here, Arthur W. Brayley's preface repeats the attribution to Mrs. Morton and supplies an assortment of conjectural biographical data about the Mortons.

In the December, 1894, issue of the *Bostonian*, Brayley first announced that the traditional ascription of the novel to Mrs. Morton

---

[6] Ibid., pp. 109–10.

[7] Francis Samuel Drake, *The Town of Roxbury* (Boston, 1878), p. 134.

had been questioned.[8] Although he did not question the attribution in his October preface, Brayley wrote in December:

> What first caused me to suspect that "Philenia" was not the author was the fact of her living in perfect happiness with her husband until his death, a circumstance that would not be countenanced by a temperament that would give to the world the details of such disgraceful affairs as those enacted in her household, and even though the identity of the real actors was concealed by fictitious names, the affair was so shocking and the persons in the real drama were so well known that the author might as well have given the correct names, so shallow was the disguise.[9]

This speculation does, of course, seem sound; however, the real agent disputing the traditional ascription was not Brayley himself, but rather a niece of William Hill Brown's still living in 1894, one Rebecca Volentine Thompson. Brayley's "informant" supplied him with information about the various children of Gawen Brown, including the fact that Brown

[8] Arthur W. Brayley, "The Real Author of 'The Power of Sympathy,'" *Bostonian* I, No. 3 (December, 1894), 224-33.
[9] Ibid., p. 229.

had written *The Power of Sympathy*. According to the story given Brayley, the Apthorps and the Browns were intimate friends. Young William was, therefore, thoroughly acquainted with all of the details of the "horrible affair" and was thus furnished with the "material for a strong story." Further, Brown's niece added an interesting, if very possibly apocryphal, anecdote:

> After the manuscript of the novel was finished, William read it to her [Catharine Byles] the day before it found its way to the hands of Mr. Isaiah Thomas, the printer.
>
> The identity of the author was soon discovered and Mr. Apthorp was greatly angered at the turn of affairs. When Mrs. Apthorp called on Mrs. Brown in reference to the subject she exclaimed, "Oh, why did Willie do such a thing when we were such good friends?"
>
> To which the latter replied, "The names are fictitious."
>
> "But," answered Mrs. Apthorp, "everybody knows whom he means." [10]

Whatever doubts one may have about this mixture of recollection and supposition, Brayley

[10] Ibid., p. 232.

was convinced by Mrs. Thompson's testimony,
and the remaining installments of the novel
appeared under William Hill Brown's name.

The first scholar to examine the problem of
the authorship of the novel was Milton Ellis.
In 1931, in collaboration with Emily Pendleton,
he published the monograph *Philenia: The Life
and Works of Sarah Wentworth Morton, 1759–
1846*. The thorough research on which the
monograph is based failed to uncover any
positive evidence identifying Mrs. Morton as
the author of *The Power of Sympathy*. Indeed,
any such hypothesis conflicts sharply with the
picture drawn of Mrs. Morton's devotion to
and pride in her family as well as her pattern
of literary activity. *Philenia* convincingly de-
stroys for all time any attempt to attribute the
novel to Mrs. Morton. In 1933 Ellis argued for
filling the void he had created with the name
of William Hill Brown.[11] In addition to the
masculine pronoun in the verse appearing on
the title page of the novel, Ellis cited two small
bits of newly discovered contemporary evidence.
The first of these is a reference in a contemporary letter in a newspaper to an "amiable youth"
as the author of the novel. Second, and perhaps

[11] Milton Ellis, "The Author of the First American Novel,"
American Literature IV (1932–33), 359–68.

more significant, is the fact that in a contemporary dramatic piece which satirizes the Mortons,
the character who represents Perez Morton
refers to the author of *The Power of Sympathy*
as *****, which can easily represent Brown.
Ellis also undertakes to defend the reliability
of Mrs. Thompson's recollections as reported
to Brayley in 1894. According to Ellis, Mrs.
Thompson was a competent authority, was in
a position to know whereof she spoke, and was
accurate concerning verifiable matters. The
circumstantial case for Brown's authorship was
thus established, but absolute proof was not
forthcoming.

It has been claimed that the presentation copy
of the novel in the Clifton Waller Barrett Collection at the University of Virginia "may be
said to have settled beyond any doubt the question of authorship." [12] The copy to which reference is made contains the following inscriptions:
[Vol. I] Mr. Wm. P. Jones. | from his friend
| & humble servant | The Author. [Vol. II]
Wm. H. Brown | to | Wm. P. Jones. Were it
possible to establish the authenticity of both of
these inscriptions, there would be absolute proof
of Brown's authorship. But the inscription in

[12] Clifton Waller Barrett, "Contemporary Collectors X:
The Barrett Collection," *Book Collector* V (1956), 223.

the second volume, the one containing Brown's name, does not match in age of ink and in handwriting that in the first volume. Apparently, the former is the product of a zealous hand who wished to transform the high degree of probability in favor of Brown's authorship into certainty. Although the seemingly authentic inscription in the first volume does establish this as a presentation copy, without the additional evidence of the second inscription this copy hardly serves as absolute proof of Brown's authorship.

A final argument supporting Brown as author is the relationship of *The Power of Sympathy* to another novel, *Ira and Isabella*, published in 1807 as "By the Late William H. Brown, of Boston." The primary plot of both novels is the same.[13] Two lovers who plan to marry are warned of the dire consequences of their union. When they ignore these warnings, they learn that because of their parents' indiscretions, their marriage would be incest. Whereas the plot of *The Power of Sympathy* ends tragically, the plot of *Ira and Isabella* ends happily when it is revealed that the lovers' fathers are not in fact one and the same. The similarity of the two works extends to details of diction, imagery,

[13] See Ellis, "The Author of the First American Novel," p. 367.

sentence structure, and even to common mis-spellings. In *Ira and Isabella* Brown was appar-ently attempting another version of the Harriot-Harrington plot in *The Power of Sympathy.*

The accumulated evidence pointing to Brown as the author of *The Power of Sympathy* pro-duces a high degree of probability that he wrote the novel. Contemporary allusions to the author are not inconsistent with the case for Brown. The first attribution of the novel to him is on the basis of apparently reliable testimony. The work fits logically into the pattern of his literary activities. Barring the discovery of new docu-mentary evidence, definite proof of Brown's authorship may never be established; until such a discovery is made, the assignment of the novel to Brown is a sound working hypothesis.

Unlike the traditional ascription of the novel to Mrs. Morton, a theory which faded quickly under the glare of scholarly investigation, an-other persistent rumor has been associated with the book. In 1850 Joseph T. Buckingham re-ferred to the fact that as soon as the novel had been published, there was a concerted attempt to suppress it, "by purchasing and destroying all the copies that could be found." [14] Mrs. Thompson's testimony to Brayley in 1894 con-

[14] Joseph T. Buckingham, *Specimens of Newspaper Litera-ture* (Boston, 1850), I, 323.

[xxiii]

firms the theory of suppression: "When the young man saw the distress caused by the publication of the story he readily agreed to stop the sale of the book and have the volumes destroyed." [15] Ellis's investigations show that if there indeed was an attempt to suppress the novel, that attempt was not totally effective. He cites advertisements in catalogues dated 1792 and 1793 and records transactions involving copies in those years.[16] He also repeats, from the Boston *Transcript* of 2 May 1867, the report of the discovery of "a dozen fresh and uncut copies in an old trunk. . . . " [17] In view of the fact that only one of the twenty odd copies extant is actually in uncut state, this "discovery" either did not take place or is reported inaccurately.

Richard Walser was the first to discover contemporary testimony referring to an attempt to suppress the novel.[18] In a scurrilous skit entitled *Occurrences of the Times. Or, the Transactions of Four Days. Viz.—From Friday the 16th, to Monday the 19th January, 1789*, Walser discovered references to *The Power of Sympathy*

[15] Brayley, op. cit., p. 232.

[16] Ellis, "The Author of the First American Novel," p. 365.

[17] Ibid., p. 366.

[18] Richard Walser, "More about the First American Novel," *American Literature* XXIV (1952–53), 352–57.

in five of the ten scenes. The most colorful reference finds Mr. Sidney's [Perez Morton's] servant Debauchee saying:

> O, Lord — O, Lord — shuch work — poor masser I pity him — He is swaring and taring, and says dam you madam to my misse, you are calm — and dare is, he says, a *Nobel* coming out nes week, cal'd the *Trumpets of Nature,* and he be dam'd if he don't blow ebery body's brains out. . . . And he says its a scrilous piece; and he will fascinate de man in de dark, and be de deth of him; and he says, dem dam'd puppys *Tedy* and *Fum,* de printers, have put a graf in de papers; and so we shall see it nes week. . . .[19]

More to the point here are Sidney's words in a later scene:

> . . . I wish to consult you upon a damn'd scurrilous Performance, that I hear is now in the booksellers hands; I would fain suppress it, if possible; I have been to the Printers, and have given them a damn'd warm dose; but for fear it should not take effect, I wish to solicit your assistance, in tracing the author of this infernal book, and try what can be done with him; for by my maker I swear, some of us must die; I cannot sup-

[19] Ibid., p. 354.

port it Sir; only think of my situation; a family and connections that are dear to me; carry your ideas a little farther, and behold my son reading a book, where his father is branded with the opprobrious epithet of villain. . . . [20]

This contemporary reference makes it clear that there was apparently some sort of attempt to suppress Brown's scandalous work. Whatever action was taken was neither thorough nor effective; new copies were available from the publisher soon thereafter and numerous copies survive today.

III

William Hill Brown was born in 1765, most probably in late November, the son of Gawen Brown and Elizabeth Hill Brown.[21] Gawen Brown had come to Boston from Northumberland, England, and made a name for himself in his adopted country as a clockmaker. Eliza-

[20] Ibid.

[21] The present account of Brown's life is based on: (1) Milton Ellis's MS notes on deposit in the University of Maine Library; (2) his biography of Brown in the *DAB*, Supplement One, pp. 125–26; (3) Richard Walser, "The North Carolina

beth Hill Adams, a widow, became his wife
after the death of his second wife, Elizabeth
Byles Brown, a daughter of Reverend Mather
Byles and great-granddaughter of Increase
Mather. Gawen Brown had two children by his
third wife: William Hill Brown and Elizabeth
(Eliza), who was to marry John Hinchborne
in 1791. William was christened at the Hollis
Street Church, Boston, on 1 December 1765.
No specific facts concerning his childhood are
recorded, but he certainly developed an interest
in literary affairs from his schooling and from
his "aunt" (actually, the half-sister of his
father's second wife), Catharine Byles. He was
acquainted with the various literary figures
active in Boston in the 1780's. He was also
obviously acquainted with Boston gossip, specifically with the tragic affair between Perez
Morton and his sister-in-law Frances Apthorp.

Brown's career as a publishing author began
in January, 1789, when he was twenty-four. In
that month *The Power of Sympathy* was issued
from the press of Isaiah Thomas. January,
1789, also witnessed the founding of Thomas's

Sojourn of the First American Novelist," *North Carolina
Historical Review* XXVIII (1951), 138–55; (4) "William Hill
Brown," *Bibliography of American Literature* I, 310–11; (5)
Arthur W. Brayley, "The Real Author of 'The Power of
Sympathy,'" *Bostonian* I (1894), 224–33.

Massachusetts Magazine, to which Brown contributed a prose tale, "Harriot: or, The Domestic Reconciliation." The scandal produced by the publication of his novel was the occasion for two minor dramatic efforts, *Occurrences of the Times* (probably not by Brown) and *The Better Sort,* which has been attributed to Brown. His contributions to periodicals include a series of literary and political essays under the title of "The Yankee," which appeared in the Boston *Columbian Centinel* from September to December, 1790. Various poetry and prose appeared in both the *Massachusetts Magazine* and the *New England Palladium,* some of which bear the pseudonym of "Pollio."

In 1792 Brown made his way south to Murfreesborough, North Carolina. His younger sister, Eliza, had married John Hinchborne in September of 1791, and the couple had moved to the Hinchborne family plantation there. Why Brown traveled thither is a matter of conjecture. Perhaps a change of scene was prescribed to bring him to his senses and make him abandon his literary pursuits for a more profitable and respectable profession. Perhaps his Bohemian inclinations threatened to produce another scandal like that which attended the

publication of his novel. In any event he headed
south, apparently with the determination to
study the law. The death of his sister in January, 1793, was the occasion for his "Elegy on
Mrs. Eliza H. . . . . ," published in the
13 March 1793 issue of the Halifax *North-
Carolina Journal.*

About this time, Brown began a study of
the law under General William Richardson
Davie in Halifax. How much of Brown's attention was actually devoted to the law is question-
able; his heart was still in letters. In the April
3 issue of the *Journal,* he published a poem
"Death of Louis XVI," signed "Columbus."
The July 3 issue of the *Journal* contained a one-
hundred-line verse fable in iambic pentameter
entitled "The Lion and the Tarapen," also
signed "Columbus." Brown's last appearance
in print during his lifetime was as the author,
again using the pseudonym "Columbus," of an
essay entitled "Education," which appeared in
the July 10 issue of the *Journal.* In this essay
Brown was defending the movement to establish the University of North Carolina, a cause
championed by his legal mentor, Davie. Toward
the end of August, 1793, an epidemic struck
the area, and Brown soon fell victim to what

was probably malaria. The September 11 issue
of the *Journal* carried the following obituary:

> DIED, after a short illness, at Murfrees-
> borough, on the 2d instant, in the 27th year
> of his age, Mr. WILLIAM HILL BROWN,
> formerly of Boston, but lately of this town,
> where he was pursuing the study of the law.
> In this gentleman were united every virtue
> and qualification, which an uncommon genius
> and insatigable [*sic*] application to study had
> rendered into general usefulness: But that
> accomplishment, which of all others shone
> conspicuously in him, and was his most prop-
> er and peculiar characteristic, was that rich-
> ness of fancy and copiousness of expression,
> which upon all occasions made him service-
> able, not only in a social but civil capacity.
> In his writings, he was concise but compre-
> hensive—sublime and elegant—a little satyri-
> cal at times, yet always pleasing and enter-
> taining—In conversation, he was affable and
> polite—witty and winning:—It will be use-
> less to illustrate his piety—the conduct of his
> life in general and his sickness in particular,
> has given sufficient testimony thereof—his
> loss is great both to his friends and country.

"Of manners gentle, of affections mild;
In wit, a man—simplicity, a child:
With Attic salt, he season'd many a page,
Form'd to delight at once and lash the age:

A good companion and a faithful friend,
Unblam'd thro' life, lamented in his *End*.
Thus say the good and worthy, with a tear,
Striking their pensive bosoms—
    BROWN *lies here*." [22]

Although Brown's life ended in Murfreesborough in 1793, he enjoyed a posthumous
literary career of sorts. In the fall of 1793, his
"aunt" Catharine Byles wrote Davie asking him
to return to her the manuscript of Brown's
play "The Tragedy of Major Andre." On 11
March 1797, "Margaret Brown, as Proprietor"
copyrighted a tragedy entitled, "West Point
Preserved or the Treason of Arnold," which
was performed at the Haymarket Theatre, Boston, in April. Brown's relatives were clearly
interested in keeping his literary productions
alive. After the passage of another decade, there
was a flurry of publication from manuscripts
by Brown unpublished at his death. A series of
verse fables and numerous other items appeared
in the *Boston Magazine* and the *Emerald* between 1805 and 1807. More important was the
publication of his second novel, *Ira and Isabella:
or The Natural Children. A Novel, Founded in*

[22] Walser, "The North Carolina Sojourn of the First American Novelist," p. 152.

[xxxi]

Fiction (Boston: Belcher & Armstrong, 1807).
Its title page states: "A Posthumous Work. By
the late William H. Brown, of Boston." After
the publication of this second novel, Brown's
name passed quickly into obscurity until his
niece stepped forward in 1894 and announced
that he was in fact the author of the first
American novel.

IV

The Power of Sympathy is not, as might be
expected, a feeble echo or slavish imitation of
a single British novel; it reflects a number of
literary influences. The epistolary form ultimately derives from Samuel Richardson, whose
Pamela (1741–42) established the propriety
of relating fiction through letters, which give
the fiction an aura of fact and at the same time
provide for easy manipulation of point of view.
In Brown's hands the epistolary technique is a
convention; his use of the device for characterization, for example, goes little further than
the intentionally bad grammar in the elder Harrington's letter-within-a-letter to Mr. Holmes
(XXXIX) and the breathless dashes which
indicate the progressive disintegration of Harrington's mind (LXIV). Nor do Brown's let-

ters attempt to preserve the illusion of being actual correspondence; there is no give and take with letter answering letter.

The importance of the theme of seduction to the plot of the novel also has antecedents in Richardson. The novel begins as though it were going to present the conventional seduction plot. Harrington is bent on removing Harriot from the protection of Mrs. Holmes to a private apartment, and we expect a series of maneuvers in which the rake assails the heroine's virtue. But Harrington's reformation comes easily, and the plot leaves the traditional seduction formula. The examination of the evils of seduction is, however, not abandoned. A long footnote in Letter XI relates the evil consequences of the seduction of Eliza Whitman, who as Eliza Wharton was to become the central figure in Hannah Webster Foster's *The Coquette* (1797). The notorious Ophelia episode (Letters XXI-XXIII and frontispiece), the story of Fidelia (Letters XXVII and XXVIII), and the "History of Maria" (Letter XXXIX) all underline the moral that "SEDUCTION is a crime . . . that nothing can be said to palliate or excuse."

Another voice which echoes through the novel is that of Laurence Sterne and the cult of sentiment and sensibility. In Letter XII a copy of Sterne's *Sentimental Journey* sets off a discussion of sentiment. The affected Miss Bourn opines that she has heard that "the bettermost genii never read any sentimental books—so you see sentiment is out of date." But Worthy jumps to the defense of Sterne: "Sentiment out of date—alas! poor *Yorick*—may thy pages never be soiled by the fingers of prejudice." . . . "These antisentimentalists would banish thee from the society of all books! Unto what a pitiful size are the race of *readers* dwindled! Surely these *antis* have no more to do with thee, than the gods of the *Canaanites*—In character and understanding they are alike—eyes have *they,* but they see not—ears have *they,* but they hear not, neither is there any knowledge to be found in them." Mrs. Holmes has earlier in the novel (Letter VII) quoted from Sterne's *Sentimental Journey*. Even the title of Brown's novel bears the mark of the cult of sensibility. The "power of sympathy" which operates in the denouement of the main plot is a result of Harriot's and Harrington's intuitive emotional awareness of their kinship.

The climax of the main plot in Harrington's suicide betrays a third major literary influence at work in *The Power of Sympathy,* that of

Goethe's *Die Leiden des jungen Werthers*. The progressively more and more gloomy letters which picture Harrington's transformation from disappointed lover to suicide parallels the decay of Werther's sanity. Brown makes the influence explicit when in Letter LXIII Worthy describes the place of Harrington's death: "A LETTER that he had written for me, laid unsealed upon the table, and *The Sorrows of Werter* was found lying by its side." If Richardson, Sterne, and Goethe are important influences on Brown's novel, there are numerous other minor literary allusions. The book is far from being a primitive work in any way and constantly reflects Brown's wide reading. Allusions to La Rochefoucault and St. Evremond; to Swift, Addison, Gay, Shakespeare, and Lord Chesterfield; to Noah Webster, Joel Barlow, and Timothy Dwight show the degree to which *The Power of Sympathy* is a literary novel.

The richness of literary allusion in *The Power of Sympathy* shows that it is the product of a sophisticated reader, but the novel is obviously the work of an unsophisticated writer. In important matters of plotting and characterization as well as in details of diction and grammar, Brown's clumsiness is all too apparent. The variety of resources at his command contained the potential for a fine novel, but the "thinness of realization" [23] meant that his finished product fell far short of greatness. But Brown was a pioneer creating the first American novel. In time, greatness was to come to the novel in America, and *The Power of Sympathy* was the first step in that direction.

[23] Leslie A. Fiedler, *Love and Death in the American Novel* (New York, 1960), p. 104.

THE
POWER OF SYMPATHY

PREFACE.

NOVELS have ever met with a ready reception into the Libraries of the Ladies, but this species of writing hath not been received with universal approbation: Futility is not the only charge brought against it. Any attempt, therefore, to make these studies more advantageous, has at least a claim upon the patience and candour of the publick.

IN Novels which *expose* no particular Vice, and which *recommend* no particular Virtue, the fair Reader, though she may find amusement, must finish them without being impressed with any particular idea: So that if they are harmless, they are not beneficial.

OF the Letters before us, it is necessary to remark, that this errour on each side has been avoided—the dangerous Consequences of SEDUCTION are exposed, and the Advantages of FEMALE EDUCATION set forth and recommended.

THE

POWER of SYMPATHY, &c.

LETTER I.

HARRINGTON *to* WORTHY.

BOSTON.

YOU may now felicitate me—I have
had an interview with the charmer I informed
you of. Alas! where were the thoughtfulness
and circumspection of my friend *Worthy?* I
did not possess them, and am graceless enough
to acknowledge it. He would have considered
the consequences, before he had resolved upon
the project. But you call me, with some degree
of truth, a strange medley of contradiction—
the moralist and the amoroso—the sentiment

[7]

and the sensibility—are interwoven in my constitution, so that nature and grace are at continual fisticuffs.————To the point:————

I PURSUED my determination of discovering the dwelling of my charmer, and have at length obtained access. You may behold my Rosebud, but should you presume to place it in your bosom, expect the force of my wrath to be the infallible consequence.

I DECLARED the sincerity of my passion—the warmth of my affection—to the beautiful *Harriot*————Believe me, *Jack,* she did not seem inattentive. Her mein is elegant—her disposition inclining to the melancholy, and yet her temper is affable, and her manners easy. And as I poured my tender vows into the heart of my beloved, a crimson drop stole across her cheek, and thus I construe it in my own favour, as the sweet messenger of hope:—

"DO not wholly despair, my new friend; excuse the declaration of a poor artless female —you see I am not perfectly contented in my situation————[Observe, *Jack,* I have not the vanity to think this distress *altogether* upon my account]————Time therefore may disclose wonders, and perhaps more to your advantage than you imagine—do not despair then."

[8]

The STORY of OPHELIA.

Sam.ˡ Hill.) Scˡ

"O Fatal! Fatal Poison!"

FRONTISPIECE TO THE FIRST EDITION OF *1789*

THE

POWER OF SYMPATHY:

OR, THE

TRIUMPH OF NATURE.

FOUNDED IN *TRUTH*.

IN *TWO* VOLUMES.

VOL. I.

FAIN would he ſtrew Life's thorny Way with Flowers,
And open to your View Elyſian Bowers ;
Catch the warm Paſſions of the tender Youth,
And win the Mind to Sentiment and Truth.

PRINTED at *BOSTON*,
BY ISAIAH THOMAS AND COMPANY.
Sold at their Bookſtore, No. 45, NEWBURY STREET.
And at ſaid THOMAS's Bookſtore in WORCESTER.
MDCCLXXXIX.

TITLE PAGE OF THE FIRST EDITION OF *1789*

SUCH vulgar, uncongenial souls, as that which animates thy clay cold carcase, would have thought this crimson drop nothing more than an ordinary blush! Be far removed from my heart, such sordid, earth-born ideas: But come thou spirit of celestial language, that canst communicate by one affectionate look—one tender glance—more divine information to the soul of sensibility, than can be contained in myriads of volumes!

HAIL gentle God of Love! While thou rivetest the chains of thy *slaves,* how dost thou make them leap for joy, as with delicious *triumph.* Happy enthusiasm! that while it carries us away into captivity, can make the heart to dance as in the bosom of content. Hail gentle God of Love! Encircled as thou art with darts, torments, and ensigns of cruelty, still do we hail thee. How dost thou smooth over the roughness and asperities of present pain, with what thou seest in reversion! Thou banishest the *Stygian* glooms of disquiet and suspense, by the hope of approaching *Elysium*—Blessed infatuation!

I DESIRE you will not hesitate to pronounce an *amen* to my Hymn to Love, as an unequivocal evidence of your wish for my success.

[9]

LETTER II.

WORTHY *to* HARRINGTON.

NEWYORK.

"WISH you success!"——In what?
Who is this lady of whom you have been talking at such an inconsistent rate? But before you have leisure to reply to these inquiries, you may have forgotten there is such a person, as she whom you call *Harriot*——I have seen many juvenile heroes, during my pilgrimage of two and twenty years, easily inflamed with new objects—agitated and hurried away by the impetuosity of new desires—and at the same time they were by no means famous for solidity of judgment, or remarkable for the permanency of their resolutions. There is such a tumult— such an ebullition of the brain in these paroxisms of passion, that this new object is very superficially examined. These, added to partiality and prepossession, never fail to blind the eyes of the lover. Instead of weighing matters maturely, and stating the evidence fairly on both sides, in order to form a right judgment,

every circumstance not perfectly coincident with your particular bias, comes not under consideration, because it does not flatter your vanity. "Ponder and pause" just here, and tell me seriously whether you are in love, and whether you have sufficiently examined your heart to give a just answer.

DO you mean to insinuate that your declaration of love hath attracted the affection of the pensive *Harriot?* If this should be the case, I wish you would tell me what you design to do with her.

LETTER III.

HARRINGTON *to* WORTHY.

BOSTON.

I CANNOT but laugh at your dull sermons, and yet I find something in them not altogether displeasing; for this reason I permit you to prate on. "Weigh matters maturely!" Ha! ha! why art thou not arrayed in canonicals! "What do I design to do with her?" Upon my word, my sententious friend, you ask mighty odd questions. I see you aim a stroke at the foundation upon which the pillar of my

new system is reared—and will you strive to
batter down that pillar? If you entertain any
idea of executing such a task, I foresee it will
never succeed, and advise you timely to desist.
What! dost thou think to topple down my
scheme of pleasure? Thou mightest as well
topple down the pike of *Teneriffe.*

I SUPPOSE you will be ready to ask, why, if I
love *Harriot,* I do not marry her—Your moni-
torial correspondence has so accustomed me to
reproof, that I easily anticipate this piece of
impertinence—But *who* shall I marry? That is
the question. *Harriot* has no father—no mother
—neither is there aunt, cousin, or kindred of
any degree who claim any kind of relationship
to her. She is companion to Mrs. *Francis,* and,
as I understand, totally dependent on that lady.
Now, Mr. *Worthy,* I must take the liberty to
acquaint you, that I am not so much of a repub-
lican as formally to wed any person of this
class. How laughable would my conduct appear,
were I to trace over the same ground marked
out by thy immaculate footsteps—To be heard
openly acknowledging for my bosom companion, any daughter of the democratick empire
of virtue!

TO suppose a smart, beautiful girl, would
continue as a companion to the best lady in
Christendom, when she could raise herself to

a more eligible situation, is to suppose a sole-cism—She might as well be immured in a nunnery. Now, *Jack,* I will shew you my be-nevolent scheme; it is to take this beautiful sprig, and transplant it to a more favourable soil, where it shall flourish and blossom under my own auspices. In a word, I mean to remove this fine girl into an elegant apartment, of which she herself is to be the sole mistress. Is not this a proof of my humanity and goodness of heart? But I know the purport of your answer—So pray thee keep thy comments to thyself, and be sparing of your compliments on this part of my conduct—for I do not love flattery. A month has elapsed since my arrival in town. What will the revolution of another moon bring forth?

Your &c.

LETTER IV.

Miss HARRIOT FAWCET *to*
Miss MYRA HARRINGTON.

BOSTON.

I HAVE somehow bewitched a new lover, my dear *Myra*—a smart, clever fellow too—and the youth expresses such fondness and passion that I begin to feel afraid even to pity him—for love will certainly follow. I own to you I *esteem* him very much, but must I go any farther? He is extremely generous—polite —gay—and I believe if you were to see him, your partiality in his favour would exceed mine.

I NEVER saw my poor swain so seemingly disconcerted and abashed as he was a few days ago—he appeared to have something very particular to communicate, but his tongue faultered —ought not one to help out a modest youth in such cases?

Your &c.

LETTER V.

Miss MYRA HARRINGTON *to Mrs.* HOLMES.

BOSTON.

ARE the rural pleasures of *Belleview,* my dear friend, so engaging as to debar us of the pleasure of your company forever? Do your dear groves, and your books, still employ your meditating mind? Serious sentimentalist as you are, let me ask, whether a Ball, a Concert or Serenade, would not afford you the satisfaction of a contemplative walk in your garden, listening to the love tales of the melodious inhabitants of the air?

RAILLERY apart—when shall I take upon myself the honour to wait upon you here?—I want to advise with you on certain points of female conduct, and about my new dress—I have heard you say, lessons to a volatile mind should be fresh and fresh applied, because it either pretends to despise them, or has a tendency to degeneracy—Now you must know I am actually degenerating for want of some of your *Mentor* like lessons of instruction. I have scarcely any opinion of my own, these fashions, changing about so often, are enough to vitiate the best taste in the world.

I FORGOT to tell you my brother has been at home this month; but, from certain indubitable symptoms, I suspect the young man to be in love.

HEIGHHO! what is become of *Worthy?* The time of my liberty steals away, for you know I was to have three or four months of liberty before I gave myself up to his authority, and relinquished all my right and title to the name of

HARRINGTON.

LETTER VI.

HARRINGTON *to* WORTHY.

BOSTON.

ABASHED—confounded—defeated—
I waited upon my beloved with my head well
furnished with ready made arguments, to pre-
vail on her to acquiesce in my benevolent
scheme—she never appeared so amiable—grace
accompanied every word she uttered, and every
action she performed. "Think, my love," said I,
in a tone something between sighing and tears,
and took her hand in a very cordial manner—
"Think, my love, on your present, unhappy,
menial situation, in the family of Mrs. *Francis.*"
I enlarged on the violence of my passion—expatiated most metaphysically on our future happiness; and concluded by largely answering
objections. "Shall we not," continued I, "obey
the dictates of nature, rather than confine ourselves to the forced, unnatural rules of———
and—and shall the halcyon days of youth slip
through our fingers unenjoyed?"

[16]

DO you think, *Worthy*, I said this to *Harriot?* —Not a syllable of it. It was impossible—my heart had the courage to dictate, but my rebellious tongue refused to utter a word—it faultered—stammered—hesitated.——

THERE is a language of the eyes—and we conversed in that language; and though I said not a word with my tongue, she seemed perfectly to understand my meaning—for she *looked*— (and I comprehended it as well as if she had *said*)——"Is the crime of dependence to be expiated by the sacrifice of virtue? And because I am a poor, unfortunate girl, must the little I have be taken from me?" "No, my love," answered I, passionately, "it shall not."

OF all those undescribable things which influence the mind, and which are most apt to persuade—none is so powerful an orator—so feelingly eloquent as beauty—I bow to the all-conquering force of *Harriot*'s eloquence—and what is the consequence?—I am now determined to continue my addresses on a principle the most just, and the most honourable.

HOW amiable is that beauty which has its foundation in goodness! Reason cannot contemplate its power with indifference—Wisdom cannot refrain from enthusiasm—and the sneering exertions of Wit cannot render it ridiculous.

[17]

There is a *dignity* in *conscious virtue* that all my impudence cannot bring me to despise—and if it be beauty that subdues my heart, it is *this* that completes the triumph—It is here my pompous parade, and all my flimsy subterfuges, appear to me in their proper light. In fine, I have *weighed matters maturely,* and the alternative is—*Harriot* must be mine, or I miserable without her.—I have so well weighed the matter that even this idea is a *flash* of joy to my heart—But, my friend, *after the lightning comes the thunder*—my father is mortally averse to my making any matrimonial engagement at so early a period—this is a bar in my way, but I must leap over it.

Adieu!

LETTER VII.

Mrs. HOLMES *to*
Miss HARRINGTON.

BELLEVIEW.

ALTHOUGH my attachment to *Belleview* is not so romantick as your airy pen has described it, I think its quiet and amusements

[18]

infinitely preferable to the bustle and parade with which you are surrounded.

THE improvements made here by my late husband (who inherited the virtues of his parents, who still protect me, and endeavour to console the anguish of his loss by the most tender affection) have rendered the charms of *Belleview* superiour in my estimation to every gilded scene of the gay world.

IT is almost vanity to pretend to give you a description of the beauty of the prospect—the grandeur of the river that rolls through the meadow in front of the house, or any eulogium on rural elegance, because these scenes are common to most places in the country. Nature is every where liberal in dispensing her beauties and her variety—and I pity those who look round and declare they see neither.

A GREAT proportion of our happiness depends on our own choice—it offers itself to our taste, but it is the heart that gives it a relish—what at one time, for instance, we think to be humour, is at another disgustful or insipid—so, unless we carry our appetite with us to the treat, we shall vainly wish to make ourselves happy. "Was I in a desart," says *Sterne,* "I would find wherewith in it to call forth my affections—If I could do no better, I would fasten them on some sweet myrtle, or seek some melancholy cypress to connect myself to—I would court their shade and greet them kindly for their protection—If their leaves withered, I would teach myself to mourn, and when they rejoiced, I would rejoice along with them."

I BELIEVE you could hardly find the way to the summer house, where we have enjoyed many happy hours together, and which you used to call "The TEMPLE of *Apollo*." It is now more elegantly furnished than it formerly was, and is enriched with a considerable addition to the library and musick.

IN front of the avenue that leads to this place, is a figure of CONTENT, pointing with one hand to the Temple, and with the other to an INVITATION, executed in such an antique style, that you would think it done either by the ancient inhabitants of the country, or by the hand of a Fairy—she is very particular in the characters she invites, but those whom she invites she heartily welcomes.

Rural Inscription.

COME YE who loath the horrid crest,
　　Who hate the fiery front of MARS;
Who scorn the mean—the sordid breast—
　　Who fly AMBITION's guilty cares:

YE who are blest with peaceful souls,
  Rest HERE: Enjoy the pleasures round;
HERE Fairies quaffe their acorn bowls,
  And lightly print the mazy ground.

Thrice welcome to this humble scene—
  (To YE alone such scenes belong)
PEACE smiles upon the fragrant green,
  And HERE the WOODLAND SISTERS throng,
And fair CONTENTMENT's pleasing train,
  Whilst in the Heav'n the stars advance,
With many a maid and many a swain,
  Lead up the jocund, rural dance.

Thrice welcome to our calm retreat,
  Where INNOCENCY oft hath strove,
With violet blue, and woodbine sweet,
  To form the votive wreath to LOVE:
O! pardon then, our cautious pride—
  (CAUTION, a virtue rare, I ween)
For evils with the great abide,
  Which dwell not in our sylvan scene.

THESE are the scenes to which I have chosen
to retreat; contented with the suffrage of the
virtuous and the good, and inattentive to the
contemptuous sneer of the giddy and the futile,
for even *these* have the vanity to look with pity

on those who voluntarily remove from whatever agrees with *their* ideas of pleasure. He who has no conception of the beauties of the mind, will contemn a person aukward or illfavoured; and one whose store of enjoyment is drawn from affluence and abundance, will be astonished at the conduct of him who finds cause to rejoice, though surrounded with inconvenience and penury. Hence we judge of the happiness of others by the standard of our own conduct and prejudices.

FROM this misjudging race I retire, without a sigh to mingle in their amusements, nor yet disgusted at whatever is thought of sufficient consequence to engage their pursuits. I fly from the tumult of the town—from scenes of boisterous pleasure and riot, to those of quietness and peace, "where every breeze breathes health, and every sound is the echo of tranquillity."—On this subject I give my sentiments to you with freedom, from a conviction that I bear the world no spleen; at the same time with a degree of deference to the judgment of others, from a conviction that I may be a little prejudiced.

I HOPE to be with you soon—in the mean time continue to write.

ELIZA HOLMES.

LETTER VIII.

WORTHY *to* HARRINGTON.

NEWYORK.

I APPLAUD your change of senti-
ment: *Harriot* is a good girl, and your conduct
is extremely praiseworthy and honourable. It is
what her virtues incontestibly merit.——But I
advise you certainly to gain your father's approbation before you proceed so far as to be
unable to return. A contrary step might terminate in the utter ruin of you both.——Direct
to me at *Belleview*—for I intend to stop there
in my return to *Boston*.

LETTER IX.

HARRINGTON *to* WORTHY.

BOSTON.

I HAVE had a conversation with my
father on the subject of early marriages, but to
no purpose—I will not be certain whether he

understood my drift, but all his arguments are applicable to my situation. One must be an adept to argue with him; and interested as he thinks himself in the result of the debate, he cannot be prevailed upon to relinquish his settled opinion. I am too much chagrined to write you even the heads of our conversation. I now stand upon my old ground.   Adieu!

LETTER X.

WORTHY *to* MYRA.

BELLEVIEW.

I AM very happy at present enjoying the sweets of *Belleview* with our excellent friend Mrs. *Holmes.* To dwell in this delightful retreat, and to be blest with the conversation of this amiable woman, cannot be called solitude. The charms of Nature are here beheld in the most luxuriant variety—it is here, diversified with a beautiful prospect, the late Mr. *Holmes* planned his garden; it is elegant, but simple. My time glides off my hands most happily—I am sometimes indulging my solitary reflections in contemplating the sublimity of the scenes around me—and sometimes in conversation with *Eliza* and the old people.

THE old gentleman is a man of a most benevolent heart; he continues to preach—is assiduous in the duties of his profession, and is the love and admiration of his flock. He prescribes for the health of the body, as well as that of the soul, and settles all the little disputes of his parish. They are contented with his judgment, and he is at once their parson, their lawyer, and their physician.——I often read in the little building that was finished by his son. He was a man of an excellent taste, and I have paid my tribute to his memory—It is the same place that you used to admire, and perhaps I improve more of my time in it on that very account.

Adieu!

LETTER XI.

Mrs. HOLMES *to* MYRA.

BELLEVIEW.

I SIT down to give you, my dear *Myra,* some account of the visitants of today, and their conversation. We are not always *dis-*

tinguished by such company, but perhaps it is sometimes necessary; and as it is a relaxation from thought, it serves to give us more pleasure in returning to the conversation of people of ideas.

MRS. *Bourn* assumes a higher rank in life than she pretended to seven years ago.—She then walked on foot—she now, by good fortune, rides in a chariot. Placed, however, in a situation with which her education does not altogether comport, she has nothing disagreeable but her over assiduity to please—this is sometimes disgusting, for one cannot feast heartily upon honey: It is an errour which a candid mind easily forgives. She sometimes appears solicitous to display her mental accomplishments, and desirous to improve those of her daughter; but it is merely apparent. Notwithstanding a temporary wish may arise towards the attainment of this point, a habitual vacancy nips it in the bud.

MISS *Bourn* is about the age of fourteen—genteel, with a tolerable share of beauty, but not striking—her dress was elegant, but might have been adjusted to more advantage—not altogether aukward in her manners, nor yet can she be called graceful—she has a peculiar air of *drollery* which takes her by fits, and for this reason, perhaps, does not avail herself of every opportunity of displaying the modesty of her sex—she has seen much company, but instead of polishing her manners, it has only increased her assurance.

THUS much of the characters of our *company.* After some small chat which passed as we took a turn in the garden, we entered the Temple.

"WHAT books would you recommend to put into the hands of my daughter?" said Mrs. *Bourn,* as she walked into the library—"it is a matter of some importance." "It is a matter of *more* importance," answered *Worthy,* "than is generally imagined, for unless a proper selection is made, one would do better never to read at all:—Now, Madam, as much depends on the choice of books, care should be taken not to put those in the way of young persons, which might leave on their minds any disagreeable prejudices, or which has a tendency to corrupt their morals."—"As obvious as your remark is," added Mr. *Holmes,* "it is evidently overlooked in the common course of education. We wisely exclude those persons from our conversation, whose characters are bad, whose manners are depraved, or whose morals are impure; but if they are excluded from an apprehension of contaminating our minds, how much more dangerous is the company of those books, where the strokes aimed at virtue are redoubled, and the poison of vice, by repeatedly reading the same thing, indelibly distains the young mind?"

"WE all agree," rejoined *Worthy,* "that it is as great a matter of virtue and prudence to be circumspect in the selection of our books, as in the choice of our company.—But, Sir, the best things may be subverted to an ill use. Hence we may possibly trace the cause of the ill tendency of many of the Novels extant."

"MOST of the Novels," interrupted my father, "with which our female libraries are overrun, are built on a foundation not always placed on strict morality, and in the pursuit of objects not always probable or praiseworthy.—Novels, not regulated on the chaste principles of true friendship, rational love, and connubial duty, appear to me totally unfit to form the minds of women, of friends, or of wives."

"BUT, as most young people read," says Mrs. *Bourn*—"what rule can be *hit upon* to make study always terminate to advantage?"

"IMPOSSIBLE," cried Miss, "for I read as much as any body, and though it may afford amusement, while I am employed, I do not remember a single word, when I lay down the book."

"THIS confirms what I say of Novels," cried Mr. *Holmes,* addressing *Worthy* in a jocular manner, "just calculated to kill time—to attract the attention of the reader for an hour, but leave not one idea on the mind."

"I AM far from condemning every production in the gross," replied *Worthy;* "general satire against any particular class, or order of men, may be viewed in the same light as a satire against the species—it is the same with books— If there are corrupt or mortified members, it is hardly fair to destroy the whole body. Now I grant some Novels have a bad tendency, yet there are many which contain excellent sentiments—let these receive their deserved reward —let those be discountenanced; and if it is impossible 'to smite them with an apoplexy, there is a moral certainty of their dying of a consumption.'——But, as Mrs. *Bourn* observes, most young persons read, I will therefore recommend to those who wish to mingle instruction with entertainment, method and regularity in reading. To *dip* into *any book* burthens the mind with unnecessary lumber, and may rather be called a disadvantage, than a benefit—The record of memory is so scrawled and blotted with imperfect ideas, that not one legible character can be traced."

"WERE I to throw my thoughts on this subject," said my good father-in-law, as he began to enter more warmly into the debate—drawing his chair opposite *Worthy,* and raising his hand with a poetical enthusiasm—"Were I to throw my thoughts on this subject into an Allegory, I would describe the human mind as an extensive plain, and knowledge as the river that should water it. If the course of the river be properly directed, the plain will be fertilized and cultivated to advantage; but if books, which are the sources that feed this river, rush into it from every quarter, it will overflow its banks, and the plain will become inundated: When, therefore, knowledge flows on in its proper channel, this extensive and valuable field, the mind, instead of being covered with stagnant waters, is cultivated to the utmost advantage, and blooms luxuriantly into a general efflorescence—for a river properly restricted by high banks, is necessarily progressive."

THE old gentleman brought down his hand with great solemnity, and we complimented him on his poetical exertion. "I cannot comprehend the meaning of this matter," said the penetrative Miss *Bourn.* "I will explain it to you, my little dear," said he, with great good nature— "If you read with any design to improve your mind in virtue and every amiable accomplishment, you should be careful to read methodically, which will enable you to form an estimate of the various topicks discussed in company, and to bear a part in all those conversations which belong to your sex—you see, therefore, how necessary general knowledge is—what would you think of a woman advanced in life, who has no other store of knowledge, than what she has obtained from experience?"

"I THINK she would have a sorry time of it;" answered Miss.

"TO prevent it in yourself," said Mrs. *Bourn* to her daughter, "be assiduous to lay in a good stock of this knowledge, while your mind is yet free from prejudice and care."

"HOW shall I *go to work,* Madam," enquired the delicate daughter.

MRS. *Bourn* turned towards Mr. *Holmes,* which was hint enough for the good old man to proceed.

"THERE is a medium to be observed," continued he, "in a lady's reading; she is not to receive every thing she finds, even in the best books, as invariable lessons of conduct; in books written in an easy, flowing style, which excel in description and the luxuriance of fancy, the imagination is apt to get heated—she ought, therefore, to discern with an eye of judgment, between the superficial and the penetrating—the elegant and the tawdry—what may be merely amusing, and what may be useful. General reading will not teach her a true knowledge of the world.

"IN books she finds recorded the faithfulness of friendship—the constancy of *true love,* and even that honesty is the best policy. If virtue is represented carrying its reward with it, she too easily persuades herself that mankind have adopted this plan: Thus she finds, when, perhaps, it is too late, that she has entertained wrong notions of human nature; that her friends are deceitful—her lovers false—and that men consult interest oftener than honesty.

"A YOUNG lady who has imbibed her ideas of the world from desultory reading, and placed confidence in the virtue of others, will bring back disappointment, when she expected gratitude. Unsuspicious of deceit, she is easily deceived—from the purity of her own thoughts, she trusts the faith of mankind, until experience convinces her of her errour—she falls a sacrifice to her credulity, and her only consolation is the simplicity and goodness of her heart.

"THE story of Miss *Whitman** is an emphatical illustration of the truth of these obser-

---

*THIS young lady was of a reputable family in *Connecticut.* In her youth she was admired for beauty and good sense. She was a great reader of novels and romances, and having imbibed her ideas of *the char-*

vations. An inflated fancy, not restricted by judgment, leads too often to *disappointment* and repentance. Such will be the fate of those who become (to use her own words)

'Lost in the magick of that sweet employ,
'To build *gay scenes* and fashion *future joy.*'

"WITH a good heart she possessed a poetical imagination, and an unbounded thirst for novelty; but these airy talents, not counterpoised with judgment, or perhaps serious reflection, instead of adding to her happiness, were the cause of her ruin."

"I CONCLUDE from your reasoning," said I, "and it is, besides, my own opinion, that many fine girls have been ruined by reading Novels."

"AND I believe," added Mrs. *Bourn,* "we may trace from hence the causes of spleen in many persons advanced in life."

"YOU mean old maids, Madam," cries the sagacious Miss, "like my aunt *Deborah*—she calls all the men deceitful, and most women, with her, are no better than they should be."

"WELL said!" exclaimed *Worthy,* "the recollection of chagrin and former disappointment,

---

acters of men, from those fallacious sources, became vain and coquetish, and rejected several offers of marriage, in expectation of receiving one more agreeable to her fanciful idea. Disappointed in her *Fairy* hope,

sours one's temper and mortifies the heart—
disappointment will be more or less severe in
proportion as we elevate our expectations; for
the most *sanguine tempers* are the soonest dis-
couraged; as the highest building is in the most
danger of falling."

"IT appears from what I have said," resumed
Mr. *Holmes,* "that those books which teach us
a knowledge of the world are useful to form
the minds of females, and ought therefore to
be studied."

I MENTIONED *Rochefoucault's* maxims.—

"DO they not degrade human nature?" enquired my father.

---

and finding her train of admirers less solicitous for
the honour of her hand, in proportion as the roses of
youth decayed, she was the more easily persuaded to
relinquish that *stability* which is the honour and happiness of the sex. The consequences of her amour becom-
ing visible, she acquainted her lover of her situation,
and a *husband* was proposed for her, who was to receive
a considerable sum for preserving the reputation of the
lady; but, having received security for the payment, he
immediately withdrew. She then left her friends, and
travelled in the stage as far as *Watertown,* where she
hired a young man to conduct her in a chaise to *Salem.*
Here she wandered alone and friendless, and at length
repaired to the *Bell-Tavern,* in *Danvers,* where she was
delivered of a lifeless child, and in about a fortnight
after (in *July,* 1788) died of a puerperal fever, aged
about 35 years.

"THIS little book," answered *Worthy,* "contains much truth——and those short sketches traced by the hand of judgment, present to us the leading features of mankind." "But," replied my father, "that *interest should assume all shapes,* is a doctrine, which, in my mind, represents a caricature rather than a living picture." "It is the duty of a painter to produce a likeness," said *Worthy.*—"And a skilful one," cried my father, continuing the metaphor, "will bring the amiable qualities of the heart to light; and throw those which disgrace humanity into the shade." "I doubt," rejoined *Worthy,* "whether this flattery will answer the purpose

---

Before her death she amused herself with reading, writing and needlework, and though in a state of anxiety, preserved a cheerfulness, not so much the effect of insensibility, as of patience and fortitude. She was sensible of her approaching fate, as appears from the following letter, which was written in characters.

"MUST I die alone? Shall I never see you more? I know that you will come, but you will come too late: This is, I fear, my last ability. Tears fall so, I know not how to write. Why did you leave me in so much distress? But I will not reproach you: All that was dear I left for you; but do not regret it.—May God forgive in both what was amiss: When I go from hence, I will leave you some way to find me; if I die, will you come and drop a tear over my grave?"

In the following Poem, she, like the dying *Swan,* sings her own Elegy, and it is here added, as a sorrow-

you aim to accomplish—You entertain a high opinion of *the dignity of human nature,* and are displeased at the author who advances any thing derogatory to that dignity. *Swift,* in speaking of these maxims, in one of his best poems, affirms,

> 'They argue no corrupted mind
> 'In him——the fault is in mankind.' "

"AS I began this subject," added I, "it shall be ended by one observation—As these maxims give us an idea of the manners and characters of men, among whom a young person is soon to appear; and as it is necessary to her security

---

ful instance, how often the best, and most pleasing talents, not accompanied by virtue and prudence, operate the destruction of their possessor.

The description of her unfortunate passion, will remind the critical reader of the famous ode of *Sappho.* In genius and in misfortune, these poetical ladies were similar.

"DISAPPOINTMENT.

"WITH fond impatience all the tedious day
I sigh'd, and wish'd the lingering hours away;
For when bright *Hesper* led the starry train,
My shepherd swore to meet me on the plain;
With eager haste to that dear spot I flew,
And linger'd long, and then with tears withdrew:
Alone, abandon'd to love's tenderest woes,
Down my pale cheeks the tide of sorrow flows;

and happiness that she be made acquainted with them—they may be read to advantage."

"THERE is another medium," said Mr. *Holmes,* assenting to my observation, "to be noticed in the study of a lady—she takes up a book, either for instruction or entertainment; the medium lies in knowing when to put it down. Constant application becomes labour—it sours the temper—gives an air of thoughtfulness, and frequently of absence. By *immoderate reading* we hoard up opinions and become insensibly attached to them; this miserly conduct sinks us to affectation, and disgustful pedantry; *conversation* only can remedy this

---

Dead to all joys that fortune can bestow,
In vain for me her useless bounties flow;
Take back each envied gift, ye pow'rs divine,
And only let me call FIDELIO mine.
  "Ah, wretch! what anguish yet thy soul must prove,
Ere thou canst hope to lose thy care in love;
And when FIDELIO meets thy tearful eye,
Pale fear and cold despair his presence fly;
With pensive steps, I sought thy walks again,
And kiss'd thy token on the verdant plain;
With fondest hope, thro' many a blissful bow'r,
We gave the soul to fancy's pleasing pow'r;
Lost in the magick of that sweet employ,
To build gay scenes, and fashion future joy,
We saw mild peace o'er fair *Canäan* rise,
And show'r her blessings from benignant skies;

dangerous evil, strengthen the judgment, and make reading really useful. They mutually depend upon, and assist each other.

"A KNOWLEDGE of HISTORY which exhibits to us in one view the rise, progress and decay of nations—which points out the advancement of the mind in society, and the improvements in the arts which adorn human nature, comes with propriety under the notice of a lady. To observe the origin of civilization—the gradual progress of society, and the refinements of manners, policy, morality and religion—to observe the progression of mankind from simplicity to luxury, from luxury to effeminacy, and the

---

On airy hills our happy mansion rose,
Built but for joy, no room for future woes;
Sweet as the sleep of innocence, the day,
(By transports measur'd) lightly danc'd away;
To love, to bliss, the union'd soul was given,
And each! too happy, ask'd no brighter heaven.
    "And must the hours in ceaseless anguish roll?
Will no soft sunshine cheer my clouded soul?
Can this dear earth no transient joy supply?
Is it my doom to hope, despair and die?
Oh! come, once more, with soft endearments come,
Burst the cold prison of the sullen tomb;
Through favour'd walks, thy chosen maid attend,
Where well known shades their pleasing branches bend,
Shed the soft poison from thy speaking eye,
And look those raptures lifeless words deny;
Still be, though late, reheard what ne'er could tire,
But, told each eve, fresh pleasures would inspire;

gradual steps of the decline of empire, and the
dissolution of states and kingdoms, must blend
that happy union of instruction and entertainment, which never fails to win our attention
to the pursuit of all subjects.

"POETRY claims her due from the ladies.
POETRY enlarges and strengthens the mind, refines the taste and improves the judgment. It
has been asserted that women have no business
with *satire*—now satire is but a branch of
poetry. I acknowledge, however, much false wit
is sent into the world, under this general title;
but no critick with whom I am acquainted ever
called satire false wit—for as long as vice and

Still hope those scenes which love and fancy drew;
But, drawn a thousand times, were ever new.
 "Can fancy paint, can words express;
 Can aught on earth my woes redress;
 E'en thy soft smiles can ceaseless prove
 Thy truth, thy tenderness and love.
 Once thou couldst every bliss inspire,
 Transporting JOY, and gay DESIRE:
 Now cold DESPAIR her banner rears,
 And PLEASURE flies when she appears;
 Fond HOPE within my bosom dies,
 And AGONY her place supplies:
 O, thou! for whose dear sake I bear,
 A doom so dreadful, so severe,
 May happy fates thy footsteps guide,
 And o'er thy *peaceful* home preside;
 Nor let ELIZA's early tomb
 Infect thee, with its baleful gloom."

[39]

folly continue to predominate in the human heart, the satirist will be considered as a useful member of society. I believe *Addison* calls him an auxiliary to the pulpit. Suffer me to enlarge on this *new idea*. Satire is the correction of the vices and follies of the human heart; a woman may, therefore, read it to advantage. What I mean by enforcing this point, is, to impress the minds of females with a principle of self correction; for among all kinds of knowledge which arise from reading, the duty of self knowledge is a very eminent one; and is at the same time, the most useful and important.

"OUR ordinary intercourse with the world, will present to us in a very clear point of view, the fallacious ideas we sometimes entertain of our own self knowledge.—We are blinded by pride and self love, and will not observe our own imperfections, which we blame with the greatest acrimony in other people, and seem to detest with the greatest abhorrence; so that it often happens, while we are branding our neighbour for some foible, or vanity, we ourselves are equally guilty.

"RIDICULOUS as this conduct must appear in the eyes of all judicious people, it is too frequently practised to escape observation.

"I WILL drop this piece of morality, with a charge to the fair reader, that whenever she discovers a satire, ridiculing or recriminating

the follies or crimes of mankind, that she look
into her own heart, and compare the strictures
on the conduct of others with her own feelings."

LETTER XII.

Mrs. HOLMES *to* MYRA.

In CONTINUATION.

My good father-in-law being so
strenuous in proving the eligibility of reading
satire, had spun out, what he called his *new
idea,* to such a metaphysical nicety, that he unhappily diminished the number of his hearers;
for Mrs. *Bourn,* to whom he directed his discourse, had taken down a book and was reading
to herself, and Miss was diverting herself with
the cuts in *Gay's* Fables.

A CONSIDERABLE silence ensued, which
Worthy first broke, by asking Mrs. *Bourn* what
book she had in her hand. Every one's atten-
tion was alarmed at this important enquiry.
Mrs. *Bourn,* with little difficulty, found the
title page, and began to read, *"A Sentimental
Journey through France and Italy, by Mr.*
Yorick."

[41]

"I DO not like the *title*," said Miss *Bourn*.

"WHY, my dear!" apostrophized the mother, "you are mistaken—it is a very famous book."

"WHY, my dear!" retorted the daughter, "It is sentimental—I abominate every thing that is sentimental—it is so unfashionable too."

"I NEVER knew before," said Mr. *Holmes*, "that wit was subject to the caprice of fashion."

"WHY 'Squire *Billy*," returned Miss, "who is just arrived from the centre of politeness and fashion, says the bettermost genii never read any sentimental books—so you see sentiment is out of date."

THE company rose to go out.——

"SENTIMENT out of date!" cries *Worthy*, repeating the words of Miss *Bourn,* and taking the book from her mother, as she walked towards the door—"Sentiment out of date—alas! poor *Yorick*—may thy pages never be soiled by the fingers of prejudice." He continued his address to the book, as they went out, in the same *Shandean* tone—"These antisentimentalists would banish thee from the society of all books! Unto what a pitiful size are the race of *readers* dwindled! Surely these *antis* have no more to do with thee, than the gods of the *Canaanites*—In character and understanding they are alike—eyes have *they,* but they see not—ears have *they,* but they hear not, neither is there any knowledge to be found in them."

"It is hardly worth while to beat it into them," said my father-in-law, "so let us follow the company."

WE did so—they walked towards the house, and *Worthy* and myself brought up the rear.

I COULD not but remark, as we went on, that Miss *Bourn* had spoken the sentiments of many of her sex;—"and whence," said I to *Worthy,* "arises this detestation of books in *some* of us females, and why are *they* enemies to any thing that may be called sentiment and conversation: I grant it often happens there is such rapidity of *speeches* that one may be at a loss to distinguish the speakers; but why is there such a calm silence, should an unfortunate sentiment inadvertantly——"

"I WILL tell you," interrupted he, "You all read, and it is from the books which engage your attention, that you generally imbibe your ideas of the principal subjects discussed in company—now, the books which employ your hours of study, happen to be Novels; and the *subjects* contained in these Novels are commonly confined to *dress, balls, visiting,* and the like *edifying* topicks; does it not follow, that these must be the subjects of your conversation? I will not dispute whether the Novel makes the woman, or the woman makes the Novel; or whether they are written to engage your attention, or flatter your vanity. I believe the result will

[43]

shew they depend, in some measure, upon each other; and an uninformed woman, by reading them, only augments the number of her futile ideas. *The female mind,* notwithstanding, *is competent to any task,* and the accomplishments of an elegant woman depend on a proper cultivation of her intelligent powers; a barrenness —a sterility of conversation—immediately discovers where this cultivation is wanting."

"GIVE me leave," answered I, "to espouse the cause of this class of females. Tell me candidly, Mr. *Worthy,* whether that insipid flattery, perhaps sacrificed at the expense of truth, does not misguide many of us into erroneous paths? You declare we are handsome—and your conduct demonstrates you to be more solicitous for the possession of *beautiful,* than of *mental* charms. Hence is the deluded female persuaded of the force of her fascinating powers, and vainly imagines one glance of her eye sufficient to reduce a million of hearts whenever she chooses: Her aims, therefore, are confined to the decoration of her person, and her views centre solely in finishing herself in those attractive, allpowerful graces, with which you declare yourselves to be enchanted. How then are they to be censured for neglecting to improve, and to adorn the mind, when your adulation diverts their attention to an external object?"

"I JOIN with you," replied *Worthy,* "in call-
ing it insipid flattery—and the vain coxcomb,
the powdered beau, the insignificant *petit
maitre,* are those who make use of it. Will
women of real merit, and sound sense, believe,
what is said by *them* to be *their* real sentiments?
—No—There must be a congeniality in the
minds of those who give and receive flattery—
Has not the vain coquette as much inclination
to be thought a goddess, as the empty admirer
to declare her so?

"FLATTERY is become a kind of epidemical
distemper; many run into it, perhaps, without
designing it, or only through civility. There are
some women who expect it—who dress to be
admired—and who deem it a mark of impolite-
ness and rudeness in men, who do not pay them
the tribute of compliment and adulation. A man
of sense *may* comply with their expectation—
he will still think them agreeable *playthings,* to
divert him at an hour of relaxation; but I
cannot suppose he will entertain any serious
thoughts of *a more permanent connexion.*

"MAY we not conclude these things to be
productive of many evils that happen in society
—do they not frighten all sentiment from conversation—introduce affectation—pride—envy
—clandestine marriages—elopements—division
of families—and ultimately terminate in the

ruin of very many innocent, but inconsiderate females?"

BY this time we had got into the house, and our company soon after departed, leaving us at full leisure to contemplate on the many wrong ideas entertained, and fallacious steps pursued by the generality of mankind, in the sentimental part of female education.

Adieu!

LETTER XIII.

WORTHY *to* MYRA.

BELLEVIEW.

A PEACEFUL, recluse life, is suited to my temper—there is something in the soft breath of Nature—in the delicacy of smiling meadows and cultivated fields—in the sublimity of an aged wood—of broken rocks—of rivers pouring along their lucid waves, to which the heart always gives a ready reception—there is something within us congenial to these scenes; they impress the mind with ideas similar to what we feel in beholding one whom we tenderly esteem.

I WAS making this observation to Mrs. *Holmes,* and she told me I was in love—"These are the very scenes," said she, "which your beloved *Myra* used to praise and admire, and for which you, by a secret sympathy, entertain the same predilection. The piece of embroidery which she worked at an early age, and which ornaments the Temple, I have seen you gaze upon several times—you seem to trace perfection in every part of it, because it was executed by the hand of *Myra.*"

I ACKNOWLEDGE I have often *gazed* upon it (as Mrs. *Holmes* terms it) but did not recollect it to be a piece of your work. I stole an opportunity to revisit it by myself, and I instantly remembered it—I remembered when you finished it, and all the happy, inoffensive scenes of our childhood, returned fresh upon my heart.

IT is the work of *Myra,* said I to myself— Did not her fingers trace these beautiful, expanding flowers?—Did not she give to this carnation its animated glow, and to this opening rose its languishing grace? Removed as I am—continued I in a certain interiour language that every son of nature possesses—Removed as I am, from the amiable object of my tenderest affection, I have nothing to do but to admire this offspring of industry and art—It shall yield more fragrance to my soul than all the *boquets* in the universe.

[47]

I DID not care to pursue the thought—it touched a delicate string—at first, however, I flattered myself I should gain some consolation—but I lost in every reflection.

I CONSIDERED the work as coming from your hand, and was delighted the more with it. A piece of steel that has been rubbed with a loadstone, retains the power of attracting small bodies of iron: So the beauties of this embroidery, springing from your hands, continue to draw my attention, and fill the mind with ideas of the artist.

Farewel!

LETTER XIV.

HARRINGTON *to* WORTHY.

BOSTON.

HOW incompetent is the force of words to express some peculiar sensations! Expression is feeble when emotions are exquisite.

I WISH you could be here to see with what ease and dignity every thing comes from the hand of *Harriot*—I cannot give a description

equivalent to the great idea I wish to convey—
You will tell me I am in love—What is love? I
have been trying to investigate its nature—to
strip it of its mere term, and consider it as it
may be supported by principle—I might as well
search for the philosopher's stone.

EVERY one is ready to praise his mistress—
she is always described in her "native simplicity," as "an angel" with a "placid mein"
"mild, animated" "altogether captivating," and
at length the task of description is given
up as altogether "undescribable." Are not all
these in themselves bare insignificant words?
The world has so long been accustomed to hear
the sound of them, that the idea is lost. But
to the question—What is love? Unless it is answered now, perhaps it never will be. Is it not
an infinitude of graces that accompany every
thing said by *Harriot?* That adorn all she does?
They must not be taken severally—they cannot
be contemplated in the abstract.—If you proceed to a chymical analysis, their tenuous
essence will evaporate—they are in themselves
nothing, but the aggregate is love.

WHEN an army composed of a great number
of men, moves slowly on at a distance, nobody
thinks of considering a single soldier.

Adieu!

LETTER XV.

HARRINGTON *to* WORTHY.

BOSTON.

AM I to believe my eyes—my ears—
my heart!—and yet I cannot be deceived.—We
are generally most stupid and incredulous in
what most materially concerns us. We find the
greatest difficulty, in persuading ourselves of
the attainment of what we most ardently desire
—She loves!—I say to myself, *Harriot* loves
me, and I reverence myself.

I THINK I may now take upon me some share
of happiness—I may say I have not lived in
vain—for all my heart holds dear is mine—
joy and love encompass me—peace and tranquillity are before me; the prospect is fair and
promising as the gilded dawn of a summer's
day—There is none to supplant me in her affection—I dread no rival, for our tempers are
similar, and our hearts beat in unison together.

Adieu!

[50]

LETTER XVI.

HARRINGTON *to* WORTHY.

BOSTON.

LOVE softens and refines the manners—polishes the asperities of aukwardness, and fits us for the society of gentle beings. It goes further, it mends the heart, and makes us better men—it gives the faint-hearted an extraordinary strength of soul, and renders them equal and frequently superiour to danger and distress.

MY passions you know are quick, my prejudices sometimes obstinate—She tells me these things are wrong—This gentle reprimand is so tempered with love that I think she commends me. I however promise a reform, and am much pleased with my improvement. *Harriot* moulds my heart into what form she chooses.

A LITTLE party is proposed tomorrow evening, and I shall attend *Harriot*. These elegant relaxations prevent the degeneracy of human nature, exhilerate the spirits, and wind up this machine of ours for another revolution of business.

LETTER XVII.

HARRINGTON *to* WORTHY.

BOSTON.

OUR little party was overthrown by a strange piece of folly. A Miss P—— was introduced, a young lady of beauty and elegant accomplishments. The whole company were beginning to be cheerful—business and care were disgusted at the sight of so many happy countenances, and had gone out from among us. Jollity and good humour bade us prepare for the dance—unhappily at this juncture a lady and gentleman were engaged in a conversation concerning Miss P——, and one of them repeated the words "a mechanick's daughter"—it is supposed the word "mechanick" was repeated scornfully—She heard it—thought herself insulted—and indignantly retired—Disorder and confusion immediately

[52]

took place, and the amusement was put an end to for the evening.

I WISH people would consider how little time they have to frolick here—that they would improve it to more advantage, and not dispute for any precedence or superiority but in good nature and sociability—"a mechanick"—and pray whence this distinction!

INEQUALITY among mankind is a foe to our happiness—it even affects our little parties of pleasure—Such is the fate of the human race, one order of men lords it over another; but upon what grounds its right is founded I could never yet be satisfied.

FOR this reason, I like a democratical better than any other kind of government; and were I a *Lycurgus* no distinction of rank should be found in my commonwealth.

IN my tour through the United States, I had an opportunity of examining and comparing the different manners and dispositions of the inhabitants of the several republicks. Those of the southern states, accustomed to a habit of domineering over their slaves, are haughtier, more tenacious of honour, and indeed possess more of an aristocratick temper than their sisters of the confederacy. As we travel to the northward, the nature of the constitution seems to operate on the minds of the people—slavery is abolished—all men are declared free and equal, and their tempers are open, generous and communicative. It is the same in all those countries where the people enjoy independence and equal liberty. Why then should those distinctions arise which are inimical to domestick quietude? Or why should the noisy voice of those who seek distinction, so loudly reecho in the ears of peace and jollity, as to deafen the sound of the musick? For while we are disputing who shall lead off the dance, behold! the instrument gets out of tune—a string snaps—and where is our chance for dancing?

Adieu!

LETTER XVIII.

HARRINGTON *to* WORTHY.

BOSTON.

MY beloved has left me for a while—she has attended Mrs. *Francis* in a journey to *Rhodeisland*—and here am I—anxious—solitary—alone!—

NO thoughts, but thoughts of *Harriot,* are permitted to agitate me. She is in my view all the day long, and when I retire to rest my imagination is still possessed with ideas of *Harriot.*

Adieu!

LETTER XIX.

HARRINGTON *to* HARRIOT.

BOSTON.

IF a wish, arising from the most tender affection, could transport me to the object of my love, I persuade myself that you would not be troubled with reading this letter.

YOU must expect nothing like wit or humour, or even common sense, from me; wit and humour are flown with you, and your return only can restore them. I am sometimes willing to persuade myself that this is the case—I think I hear the well known voice, I look around me with the ecstacy of *Orpheus,* but that look breaks the charm, I find myself alone, and my *Eurydice* vanished to the shades.

I HOPE you will not permit yourself to grow envious of the beauties of *Rhodeisland*. Of the force of their charms I am experimentally acquainted. Wherever fortune has thrown me, it has been my happiness to imagine myself in love with some divine creature or other; and after all it is but truth to declare that the passion was seated more in fancy than the heart; and it is justice to acknowledge to you that I am now more provident of my passion, and never suffer the excursion of fancy, except when I am so liberal as to admit the united *beauty* of the *Rhodeisland* ladies in competition with yours.

WHERE there are handsome women there will necessarily be fine gentlemen, and should they be smitten with your *external graces,* I cannot but lament their deplorable situation, when they discover how egregiously they have been cheated. What must be his disappointment, who thought himself fascinated by beauty, when he finds he has unknowingly been charmed by reason and virtue!

BUT this you will say contains a sentiment of jealousy, and is but a transcript of my apprehensions and gloomy anxieties: When will your presence, like the return of the sun in the spring, which dispels glooms, and reanimates the face of nature, quiet these apprehensions.

[56]

If it be not in a short time, I shall proceed on a journey to find you out; until then I commit you to the care of your guardian angel.

LETTER XX.

HARRINGTON *to* HARRIOT.

BOSTON.

LAST night I went on a visit to your house: It was an adventure that would have done honour to the Knight of *La Mancha*. The moon ascended a clear, serene sky, the air was still, the bells sounded the solemn hour of midnight—I sighed—and the reason of it I need not tell you. This was, indeed, a pilgrimage; and no *Musselman* ever travelled barefooted to *Mecca* with more sincere devotion.

YOUR absence would cause an insufferable *ennui* in your friends, were it not for the art we have in making it turn to our amusement. Instead of wishing you were of our party, you are the goddess to whose honour we perform innumerable *Heathenish* rites. Libations of wine are poured out, but not a guest presumes

[57]

to taste it, until they implore the name of *Harriot;* we hail the new divinity in songs, and strew around the flowers of poetry. You need not, however, take to yourself any extraordinary addition of vanity on this occasion, as your absence will not cause any repining:

"HARRIOT, our goddess and our grief no more."

BUT to give you *my* opinion on this important matter, I must descend to plain truth, and acknowledge I had rather adore you a *present* mortal, than an *absent* divinity; and therefore wish for your return with more religious ardour than a devout disciple of the false prophet for the company of the *Houri.*

THANKS to the power of imagination for one fanciful interview. Methought I somewhere unexpectedly met you—but I was soon undeceived of my imaginary happiness, and I awoke, repeating these verses:—

THOUGH sleep her sable pinions spread,
  My thoughts still run on you;
And visions hovering o'er my head,
  Present you to my view.

By FANCY's magick pencil drest,
  I saw my *Delia* move;
I clasp'd her to my anxious breast,
  With TEARS of joy and love.

Methought she said—"Why thus forlorn?—
Be all thy care resign'd:"——
I 'woke and found my *Delia* gone,
But still the TEAR behind.

LETTER XXI.

HARRIOT *to* MYRA.

RHODEISLAND.

WE arrived here in safety, but our
journey is not without incident—an incident
which exhibits a melancholy picture of the
wickedness and depravity of the human heart.

WHEN we came to the house of Mrs. *Martin,*
who, I suppose you know is cousin to Mrs.
Francis, we were not a little astonished at the
evident traces of distress in her countenance;
all her actions were accompanied with an air
of solemnity, and her former gaiety of heart
was exchanged for sad, serious thoughtfulness:
She, however, put on a face of vivacity upon
our being introduced, but her cheerfulness was
foreign to the feelings of her heart.

MR. *Martin* was equally agitated; he endeavoured to dispossess himself of an *uncommon*

[59]

weight of remorse, but in vain—all his dissimulation could not conceal his emotion, nor
his art abate the continual upbraidings of
conscious guilt.

MRS. *Francis* was anxious to enquire the
cause of this extraordinary change, but wisely
forebore adding to the distress of her friend,
by desiring her to explain it, in a manner
too precipitate. She was in a short time made
acquainted with the particulars of the story—
which is not more melancholy than uncommon.

SOMETIME after the marriage of *Martin,* the
beautiful *Ophelia,* sister to Mrs. *Martin,* returned from an *European* visit, to her friends
in *Rhodeisland.* Upon her arrival, she received
a polite offer from her brother-in-law of an
elegant apartment at his house in town, which
was cheerfully accepted—Fatal acceptation! He
had conceived a passion for *Ophelia* and was
plotting to gratify it. By a series of the most
artful attentions, suggested by a diabolical appetite, he insinuated himself into her affection—
he prevailed upon the heart of the unsuspicious
Ophelia, and triumphed over her innocence and
virtue.

THIS incestuous connexion has secretly subsisted until the present time—it was interrupted
by a symptom which rendered it necessary for
Ophelia to retire into the country, where she

was delivered of a child, at once the son and nephew of *Martin*.

THIS event was a severe mortification to the proud spirit of *Shepherd,* the father of *Ophelia.* His resentment to his daughter was implacable, and his revenge of the injury from *Martin* not to be satiated. The blaze of family dispute raged with unquenchable fury—and poor *Ophelia* received other punishment from the hand of a vindictive father than bare recrimination.

THE affection of *Martin* now became changed to the vilest hatred.

THUS doomed to suffer the blackest ingratitude from her seducer on the one hand, and to experience the severity of paternal vengeance on the other—and before her the gloomy prospect of a blasted reputation—what must be the situation of the hapless *Ophelia!* Hope, the last resort of the wretched, was forever shut out. There was no one whom she durst implore by the tender name of father, and he who had seduced her from her duty and her virtue, was the first to brand her with the disgraceful epithets, of undutiful and unchaste.

PERHAPS it was only at this time, that she became fully sensible of her danger; the flattery and dissimulation of *Martin* might have banished the idea of detection, and glossed over that of criminality; but now she awoke from her dream of insensibility, she was like one who had been deluded by an *ignis fatuus* to the brink of a precipice, and there abandoned to his reflection to contemplate the horrours of the sea beneath him, into which he was about to plunge.

WHETHER from the promises of *Martin,* or the flattery of her own fancy, is unknown, but it is said she expected to become his wife, and made use of many expedients to obtain a divorcement of *Martin* from her sister: But this is the breath of rumour. Allowing it to be truth, it appears to be the last attempt of despair; for such unnatural exertions, with the compunction attending them, represent a gloomy picture of the struggle between sisterly affection and declining honour. They however proved unavailable, and her efforts to that end, may with propriety be deemed a wretched subterfuge.

IN the mean while the rage of *Shepherd* was augmenting. Time, instead of allaying, kindled the flame of revenge in the breast of the old man. A sense of the wounded honour of his family, became every day more exquisite; he resolved to call a meeting of the parties, in which the whole mystery should be developed— that *Ophelia* should confront her seducer, and a thorough enquiry and explication be brought about.

OPHELIA exercised all her powers to prevent it; she intreated her father to consent to her desire, but her tears and intreaties were vain. To this earnest desire of his daughter, *Shepherd* opposed the honour of his family. She replied that such a procedure would publish its disgrace and be subversive of his intention: That she hoped to live retired from the world, and it was in his power to accept her happy repentance: In extenuating, she wished not to vindicate her errours, but declared herself to be penetrated with a melancholy sense of her misconduct, and hoped her penitence might expiate her guilt: She now beheld in the most glaring colours, the dangers to which she had been exposed, and acknowledged the effects of her temerity had impressed her mind with sincere contrition: All persons, continued she, are not blest with the like happiness of resisting temptation; she intreated her father, therefore, to believe her misfortunes proceeded from credulity and not from an abandoned principle— that they arose more from situation than a depraved heart: In asking to be restored to the favour and protection of a parent, she protested she was not influenced by any other motive, than a wish to demonstrate the sincerity of her repentance, and to establish the peace and harmony of the family.

OPHELIA now became melancholy, and her intentions visibly bent on the *manner of her death*. As the time drew nigh, her sensibility became more exquisite: What was before distress, she now averred to be horrour: Her conduct bordered upon insanity.

THE day was appointed to bring to a settlement this unhappy business—the time of hearing arrived—the parties met—the presence of *Ophelia* was necessary—she was missing—the unfortunate *Ophelia* died by her own hand.

MRS. *Shepherd* entered the apartment of her daughter—she beheld her pale and trembling—she saw the vial, and the cup with the remains of the poison—she embraced her lost child—"My *Ophelia!* my daughter! return—return to life."

AT this crisis entered the father—he was mute—he beheld his daughter struggling with the pangs of dissolution—he was dumb with grief and astonishment.

THE dying *Ophelia* was conscious of the distress of her parents, and of her own situation—she clasped her mother's hand, and raising her eye to heaven, was only heard to articulate "LET

MY CRIME BE FORGOTTEN WITH MY NAME.—O
FATAL! FATAL POISON!"

ADIEU! my dear *Myra*—this unhappy affair
has worked me into a fit of melancholy. I can
write no more. I will give you a few particulars
in my next. It is impossible to behold the effects
of this horrid catastrophe and not be impressed
with feelings of sympathetick sorrow.

LETTER XXII.

HARRIOT *to* MYRA.

RHODEISLAND.

How frail is the heart! How dim is
human foresight! We behold the gilded bait of
temptation, and know not until taught by experience, that the admission of one errour is
but the introduction of calamity. One mistake
imperceptibly leads to another—but the consequences of the whole bursting suddenly on the
devoted head of an unfortunate wanderer, becomes intolerable. How acute must be that
torture, which seeks an asylum in suicide! O

SEDUCTION! how many and how miserable are the victims of thy unrelenting vengeance. Some crimes, indeed, cease to afflict when they cease to exist, but SEDUCTION opens the door to a dismal train of innumerable miseries.

YOU can better imagine the situation of the friends of the unfortunate *Ophelia* than I can describe it.

THE writings she left were expressive of contrition for her past transaction, and an awful sense of the deed she was about to execute. Her miserable life was insupportable, there was no oblation but in death—she welcomed death, therefore, as the pleasing harbinger of relief to the unfortunate. She remembered her once loved seducer with pity, and bequeathed him her forgiveness—To say she felt no agitation was not just, but that she experienced a calmness unknown to a criminal was certain. She hoped the rashness of her conduct would not be construed to her disadvantage—for she died in charity with the world. She felt like a poor wanderer about to return to a tender parent, and flattered herself with the hopes of a welcome, though unbidden to return. She owned the way was dark and intricate, but lamented she had no friend to enlighten her understanding, or unravel the mysteries of futurity. She knew there was a God who will reward and punish: She acknowledged she had offended him, and confessed her repentance. She expatiated on the miserable life she had *suffered,* not that she feared detection, that was impossible; but that she had been doing an injury to a sister who was all kindness to her; she prayed her sister's forgiveness—even as she herself forgave her seducer; and that her crime might not be called ingratitude, because she was always sensible of her obligation to that sister. She requested her parents to pardon her, and acknowledged she felt the pangs of a bleeding heart at the shock which must be given to the most feeling of mothers. She intreated her sisters to think of her with pity, and died with assurance that her friends would so far revere her memory as to take up one thing or another, and say this belonged to poor *Ophelia.*

O MY friend! what scenes of anguish are here unfolded to the survivours. The unhappy *Shepherd* charged *Martin* with the seduction and murder of his daughter. What the termination of this most horrible affair will be, is not easy to foresee.

Adieu!

LETTER XXIII.

HARRIOT *to* MYRA.

RHODEISLAND.

WHATEVER may be the other causes (if there were any besides her seduction) which drove the unhappy *Ophelia,* temerariously to end her existence, it certainly becomes us, my dear friend, to attend to them— and to draw such morals and lessons of instruction from each side of the question, as will be a mirrour by which we may regulate our conduct and amend our lives. A prudent pilot will shun those rocks upon which others have been dashed to pieces, and take example from the conduct of others less fortunate than himself: It is the duty of the moralist, then, to deduce his observations from preceding facts in such a manner as may directly improve the mind and promote the economy of human life.

THIS may be an apology for sending you the arguments of *Martin* in answer to *Shepherd,* who in his rage and grief had called him the murderer of his child.

HE reminded *Shepherd* of his obstinacy in *persisting* in an explanatory meeting, and refusing to grant *Ophelia's* request in suffering the affair to subside—"Your proud spirit," said he, "would not hearken to the gentle remonstrance of your daughter—your heart was closed to every conciliatory proposition. Though she expressed a propensity to fly from the eye of the world, she had hitherto appeared lulled in a kind of happy insensibility; yet the approaching time of explanation was terrible, it renewed the story and torture of all her misfortunes, and the idea filled her with grief and dismay. Had you been as willing to receive her, as she to return to you, happy would it have been for both; but your pride was the cause of additional calamities—when the time arrived—But why shall we harrow up our souls with the reiteration of her sorrowful exit?——

"FROM these circumstances," said *Martin,* "you cannot accuse me as the *immediate* cause of *Ophelia's* death; the facts are as I have stated them—and thus was a straying, but penitent child, driven to despair and suicide by a severe use of paternal power, and a vain attempt to resent an injury, for which it was impossible the accused party could make compensation."

NOTWITHSTANDING the plausibility of *Martin*'s plea, I have little hesitation in my mind to charge him with the *remote cause* of the miserable end of *Ophelia*.

HOW far parental authority may be extended, is a question which I shall not determine; I must however think it depends upon the combination of circumstances. The duty of a child to her parents will be in proportion to the attention paid to her education. If, instead of the usual pains bestowed by many partial parents, upon the vain parade of forming the manners of a child, and burthening the mind with the *necessity* of the douceurs and the graces, would it not often be happier for both, to take a small share of thought to kindle *one spark of grace* in the heart?

HAPPY the parents, who have bestowed upon their children such an education, as will enable them, by a principle of mediocrity, to govern them without extorting obedience, and to reclaim them without exercising severity.

Farewel!

LETTER XXIV.

HARRIOT *to* MYRA.

RHODEISLAND.

MRS. *Francis* is not altogether satisfied with her journey to this part of the country —She does not delight to brood over sorrow— She flies from the house of mourning, to scenes of dissipation, congenial to her temper and disposition—and, like the rest of the world, bears the misfortunes of her friends with a most christian fortitude: The melancholy aspect of affairs here, will therefore shorten our visit— so you may expect us at *Boston* in a few days.

MY faithful lover (with whom I will certainly make you acquainted in a short time) continues to write to me in very passionate and sentimental strains. His last letter proves him to be a *tolerable maker of rhymes,* and I inclose it* for your *entertainment.*

I am, my dear,

Your most affectionate Friend.

*See Letter XX.

[71]

LETTER XXV.

MYRA *to* HARRIOT.

(Written before she had received the preceding.)

BOSTON.

YOUR sorrowful little history has infected me with grief. Surely there is no human vice of so black a die—so fatal in its consequences—or which causes a more general calamity, than that of *seducing* a female from the path of honour. This idea has been improved by my brother, on the hint of your favour—as an acknowledgment for which I inclose you his production.

[The Inclosed.]

The Court of Vice.

An APOLOGUE.

VICE "on a solemn night of state,
In all her pomp of terrour sate,"
Her voice in deep, tremendous tone,

[72]

Thus issu'd from her ebon throne:
'This night at our infernal court,
'Let all our ministers resort;
'Who most annoys the human race,
'At our right hand shall take his place,
'Rais'd on a throne—advanc'd in fame—
'Ye CRIMES now vindicate your claim.'

Eager for praise, the hideous host,
All spake, aspiring to the post.

PRIDE said, to gain his private ends,
He sacrific'd his dearest friends;
Insulted all with manners rude,
And introduc'd ingratitude.
'Twas he infus'd *domestick* hate,
And party spirit in the *state;*
Hop'd they'd observe his mystick plan,
Destroy'd all confidence in man;
And justify'd his high pretentions,
By causing envy and dissentions.

INTEMP'RANCE loud, demands the place,
He'd long deceiv'd the human race;
None could such right as he maintain,
Disease and death were in his train.

THEFT next appears to claim the station,
E'er constant in his dark vocation;
He thought the place might well repay,
The *crime* who labour'd night and day.

FRAUD own'd (tho' loth to speak his praise)
He gain'd his point by secret ways;
His voice in cities had been heard,
And oft in senates been preferr'd!
Yet much derision had he borne,
Treated by honest fools with scorn;
His influence on the western shore
Was not so great as heretofore:
He own'd each side alike assail'd,
Complain'd how sadly he was rail'd,
Curst by the name in ev'ry street,
Of Paper, Tendry, Rogue and Cheat:
Yet if some honour should requite
His labour—things might still go right.

MURDER before the footstool stood,
With tatter'd robe distain'd in blood.
'And who,' he cry'd, with daring face,
'Denies my title to the place?
'My watchful eyes mankind survey,
'And single out the midnight prey;
'Not cowardlike I meet the foe,
'With footsteps insecure and slow,
'Or cause his death by languid strife—
'Boldly this dagger ends his life.
'Give back, ye CRIMES, your claims resign,
'For I demand the post as mine.'

AV'RICE declar'd his love of gold;
His nation, or himself he sold;
He taught the sin of PRIDE betimes;
Was foster-father of all *crimes:*
He pawn'd his life; he stak'd his soul,
And found employment for the whole:
Acknowledg'd that he gain'd his wealth,
By FRAUD, by MURDER and by STEALTH:
On one so useful in her cause,
VICE well might lavish due applause.

The hagger'd host bow low the head,
The *Monster* rose, and thus she said:
'Ye *ministers of* VICE, draw near,
'For fame no longer persevere;
'No more your various parts disclose,
'Men *see, and hate you all as foes.*
'One yet remains among your crew,
'Then rise, SEDUCTION! claim your due.
'Your baleful presence quickly parts
'The tie that holds the happiest hearts;
'You *rob*—what *wealth* can ne'er repay;
'Like *Judas* with a kiss *betray:*
'Hence come the starving, trembling train,
'Who prostitute themselves for gain,
'Whose languid visages impart
'A smile, while anguish knaws the heart;

[75]

'Whose steps decoy unwary youth,
'From honour, honesty, and truth,
'Which follow'd 'till too late to mend,
'In ruin, and the gallows end—
'Be thine the post. Besides, who knows
'Where all thy consequences close?
'With thee, SEDUCTION! are ally'd
'HORROUR, DESPAIR and SUICIDE.
'YOU wound—but the *devoted* heart
'Feels not alone—the poignant smart:
'YOU wound—th' electrick pain extends
'To fathers, mothers, sisters, friends.
'MURDER may yet delight in blood,
'And deluge round the crimson flood;
'But sure his merits rank above,
'Who murders in the mask of love.'

LETTER XXVI.

MYRA *to* Mrs. HOLMES.

BOSTON.

IN one of my former letters I acquainted you that I suspected my brother to
be in love, and now, Madam, I am enabled to
tell you with whom—the amiable *Harriot*.

HARRIOT attended Mrs. *Francis* in her journey to *Rhodeisland*, and our young hero has, in her absence, been dreaming of his mistress; and, in a letter to her has written a description of his visionary interview. *Harriot,* with whom I maintain a constant correspondence, and who keeps no secret from me, inclosed the verses in her last, when lo! the hand writing of Master *Harrington.*

I WAS a little mortified that the young man had kept me in ignorance of his amour all this time, and this morning determined upon a little innocent revenge—*"Tommy,"* said I, as he entered the room, "here is a piece of poetry, written by an acquaintance of mine—I want your judgment on it"—"Poetry or rhyme," answered he, advancing towards me, and casting his eye on it—He took the letter and began to read——"Why do you blush, young man?" said I, *"Harriot* is a fine girl."——

THIS produced an *eclaircissement,* and as the matter must remain secret, for a certain weighty reason, I am to be the *confidante.*

I MUST acknowledge to you, Mrs. *Holmes,* there is a certain *je ne sçais quoi* in my amiable friend, that has always interested me in her favour—I have an affection for her which comes from the heart—an affection which I do not pretend to account for—Her dependance on Mrs. *Francis* hurts me—I do not think this lady is the gentle, complaisant being, that she appears to be in company—To behold so fine a girl in so disagreeable a situation, might at first attract my commiseration and esteem, and a more intimate knowledge of her virtues might have ripened them into love. Certain it is, however, that whom I admire as a friend, I could love as a SISTER. In the feelings of the heart there can be no dissimulation.

PLEASE to tell Mr. *Worthy,* he may continue to write, and that I will condescend to read his letters.

Farewel!

LETTER XXVII.

WORTHY *to* MYRA.

BELLEVIEW.

I AM just returned from a melancholy excursion with *Eliza.* I will give you the history of it—We generally walk out together, but we this time went further than usual—The morning was calm and serene—all Nature was flourishing, and its universal harmony conspired to deceive us in the length of the way.

WHILE we were pursuing our walk, our ears were struck with a plaintive, musical voice, singing a melancholy tune.—"This," said Mrs. *Holmes,* "must be *Fidelia*—the poor distracted girl was carried off by a ruffian a few days before her intended marriage, and her lover, in despair, threw himself into the river"—*Eliza* could say no more—for *Fidelia* resumed her melancholy strain in the following words:——

> TALL rose the lily's slender frame,
> It shed a glad perfume;
> But ah! the cruel spoiler came,
> And nipt its opening bloom.
>
> Curse on the cruel spoiler's hand
> That stole thy bloom and fled—
> Curse on his hand—for thy true love
> Is number'd with the dead.
>
> Poor maiden! like the lily frail,
> 'Twas all in vain you strove;
> You heard the stranger's tender tale—
> But where was thy true love?
>
> Thou wast unkind and false to him,
> But he did constant prove;
> He plunged headlong in the stream—
> Farewel, farewel, my love!

[79]

'Twas where the river rolls along,
　　The youth all trembling stood,
Opprest with grief—he cast himself
　　Amidst the cruel flood.

White o'er his head the billows foam,
　　And circling eddies move;
Ah! there he finds a watery tomb—
　　Farewel, farewel, my love!

WE advanced towards the place from whence
the sound issued, and *Fidelia,* who heard our
approach, immediately rose from the ground;
"I was tired," said she, "and sat down here to
rest myself."

SHE was dressed in a long white robe, tied
about the waist with a pink ribband; her fine
brown hair flowed loosely round her shoulders
—In her hand she held a number of wild flowers and weeds, which she had been gathering.
"These," she cried, "are to make a nosegay for
my love." "He hath no occasion for it," said
Eliza. "Yes! where he lives," cried *Fidelia,*
"there are plenty—and flowers that never fade
too—I will throw them into the river, and they
will swim to him—they will go straight to him"
—"And what will he do with them?" I asked.
"O!" said the poor girl as she looked wistfully
on them, and sorted them in her hand, "he loves

every thing that comes from me—he told me so"—"He will be happy to receive them," cried *Eliza*—"Where he is," said *Fidelia,* "is happiness—and happy are the flowers that bloom there—and happy shall I be, when I go to him—alas! I am very ill now"—"He will love you again," said *Eliza,* "when you find him out"—"O he was very kind," cried she, tenderly, "he delighted to walk with me over all these fields—but now, I am obliged to walk alone." *Fidelia* drew her hand across her cheek, and we wept with her.—"I must go," she said, "I must go," and turned abruptly from us, and left us with great precipitation.

Farewel!

LETTER XXVIII.

WORTHY *to* MYRA.

BELLEVIEW.

M Y melancholy meditations led me yesterday to the same place where I had seen the distracted *Fidelia,* and walking down the hill I again beheld her by the side of a beautiful spring—Before I could come up to the place,

she was gone—she went hastily over the field—
I followed her—after a few minutes walk, I
overtook her, and we both went on together
towards a small, neat, farm house. An old man
was sitting at the door—he gave a sigh as she
passed by him to go in—I asked him if she was
his daughter—"Alas!" said he, "my poor child
—she has been in this state of affliction for
near a twelve month." I inquired what cause
produced the loss of her senses—He looked
down sorrowfully—the question awakened the
gloomy sensations of past evils, the recollection
of which was painful, and opened wounds
afresh that were not yet healed. "She has lost
her lover," cried the old man—"the youth was
the son of one of our neighbours—their infancy
was marked by a peculiar attachment to each
other. When the young people danced together,
Fidelia was always the partner of *Henry*—as
they grew up their mutual tenderness ripened
into passionate affection. They were engaged
to each other, and *Henry* saved all his little
stock of money to begin the world by himself.
All the town beheld them with pleasure—they
wished them success and happiness—and from
their knowledge of both their characters, were
led to hope they would one day become good
members of society—but these hopes are
blasted, and they now bestow the bitterest

curses on the wretch who hath crushed their expectations—who hath deprived *Fidelia* of her senses, and caused the death of her lover.

"THE gay *Williams* comes among us, and participates in our domestick pastimes—he singles out *Fidelia,* and is assiduous in his attentions to her—her little heart is lifted up—but her prudence rises superiour to her vanity. *Henry* observes the operations of *Williams* and thinks he sees in him a powerful rival—the unhappy youth becomes melancholy—he sickens with jealousy—the pleasures of our country are forgotten by him—his thoughts are continually employed on his *Fidelia.*—To complete the measure of his promised happiness he wishes to call her his own—he declares the desire of his soul—*Fidelia* pledges her faith. He now sees the accomplishment of all his wishes in reversion—his heart leaps for joy—but—as the little paraphernalia is preparing, the ruffian hand of the Seducer dashes the cup of joy from their lips—*Fidelia* suddenly disappears—*Williams*—the ungrateful *Williams*—betrays her to a carriage he had prepared, and she is hurried off. *Henry* stands astonished—wild with grief and dismay, he appears senseless and confounded.

"WHEN the heart is elevated by strong expectation—disappointment and misfortune come with redoubled force—To receive pain, when we look for pleasure, penetrates the very soul with accumulated anguish."

THE old man paused——He endeavoured to hide a tear that was stealing down his cheek—and to check the violence of his passion.

I ASKED him how long his daughter was missing—"Not long," he answered—"the young men, enraged at the insult, arm themselves and pursue the robber—they overtake him—*Williams* is wounded in the scuffle, and is carried away bleeding, by his servant—My daughter is regained—we thank Heaven for her restoration. She enquires for her *Henry*—alas! *Henry* is no more! The object of his love had flown from him, and with her, all the light of his soul—Darkness and grief had encompassed him—he had no resource, no consolation, no hope—she whom his soul loved was stolen—was wrested from his embrace. Who was there to administer relief?—Who was there to supply her loss?—Not one.—The light of his reason now became clouded—he is seized by despair, and urged forward by the torments of disappointed love, he plunges into the river—to close his sorrows with his life.

"THE loss of *Fidelia*'s senses followed this tragical event.

"SHE hears the fate of her lover and becomes petrified—the idea of her sorrows—her own agitation and care for her person, are lost in the reflection of her lover's death.—A while she raved—but is now somewhat restored, and, as you see, the poor maniack strays about the fields harmless and inoffensive."

THE old man proceeded to inform me of the death of his wife—the idea of one misfortune aroused in him that of another—or rather there was a gradual progression in them, and consequently a connexion—He told me she did not long survive the death of *Henry.* "O *Charlotte!*" he cried, "thou wast kind and cheerful—very pleasant hast thou been unto me. I will not cease to regret thy loss, till I meet thee in a better world."

"OUR hearts," continued the old man, addressing me, "are loosened from their attachment to this world by repeated strokes of misfortune. Wisely is it ordered thus. Every calamity severs a string from the heart—until one scene of sorrow on the back of another, matures us for eternity—Thus are our affections estranged from this scene of misery. The cord that detains the bird is severed in two—and it flies away.

"FORMERLY as I sat in this place—in the mild shade of the evening—when I had returned from my labour and took *Fidelia* on my knee, how often have I rendered thanks to Heaven for the happiness I enjoyed, and implored his power to make my child such another as *Charlotte*—This sweet remembrance yet swells and agitates my heart, and in the midst of the distress which surrounds me, I feel a consolation in tracing to you a feeble sketch of the happy times that are passed."

THE old man was sensibly affected—he delighted to dwell on what his child had been—he thought of those times—and he sighed when he contrasted them with the present.

"IN her disordered state," continued he, "she knows me not as a father—I spread my morsel before her, and she flies from it—she forgets the sound of my voice—she is no longer unto me as a daughter. She who hath so often said, she would support me with her arm, and lead me about, when I should be old and decriped—to her I call, but she returns me no answer. Is not the cause of my woe, a melancholy instance of the baleful art of the SEDUCER?—She is deprived of her reason, and knows not the weight of her misery; and I am doubly burdened with her affliction, and the accumulated misfortune of immature decripitude."

"SEDUCTION is a crime," I observed, "that nothing can be said to palliate or excuse."

"AND wo to him," added the old man, "who shall endeavour to extenuate it——*They have*

taken away my staff"—continued he, raising a
look of imploring mercy to Heaven, while a
trembling tear rolled from his swollen eye,
*"They have taken away my staff in my old
age."*

FREELY did my heart share in the sorrows of
the good old man—when I left him, I prayed
Heaven to compassionate his distress—and as
I bent my pensive step towards *Belleview,* I had
leisure to animadvert on the fatal tendency of
SEDUCTION.

Adieu!

LETTER XXIX.

Mrs. HOLMES *to* MYRA.

BELLEVIEW.

I AM sometimes mortified to find the
books which I recommend to your perusal, are
not always applicable to the situation of an
American lady. The general observations of
some *English* books are the most useful things
contained in them; the principal parts being

chiefly filled with local descriptions, which a young woman here is frequently at a loss to understand.

I SEND you a little work, entitled *"A Lady of Quality's Advice to her Children"* which, though not altogether free from this exception, is highly worthy of your attention. A parent who is represented struggling with the distress of a lingering illness, bequeaths a system of education to her offspring. I do not recommend it to you as a Novel, but as a work that speaks the language of the heart and that inculcates the duty we owe to ourselves, to society and the Deity.

DIDACTICK essays are not always capable of engaging the attention of young ladies. We fly from the laboured precepts of the essayist, to the sprightly narrative of the novelist. Habituate your mind to remark the difference between truth and fiction. You will then always be enabled to judge of the propriety and justness of a thought; and never be misled to form wrong opinions, by the meretricious *dress* of a pleasing tale. You will then be capable of deducing the most profitable lessons of instruction, and the design of your *reading* will be fully accomplished.——

HENCE you will be provided with a key to the characters of men: To unlock these curious cabinets is a very useful, as well as entertaining employment. Of those insidious gentlemen, who plan their advances towards us on the *Chesterfieldian* system, let me advise you to beware. A prudent commander would place a double watch, if he apprehended the enemy were more disposed to take the fort by secresy and undermining, than by an open assault.

I CANNOT but smile sometimes, to observe the ridiculous figure of some of our young gentlemen, who affect to square their conduct by his Lordship's principles of politeness—they never tell a story unless it be very short—they talk of decorum and the *etiquette*—they detest every thing vulgar or common—they are on the rack if an old man should let fall a proverb—and a thousand more trifling affectations, the ridicule of which arises, not so much from their putting on this foreign dress, as from their ignorance or vanity in pretending to imitate those rules which were designed for an English nobleman—Unless, therefore, they have a prospect of being called by Congress to execute some foreign negociation, they ought certainly to be minding their business.

THIS affectation of fine breeding is destructive to morals. Dissimulation and insincerity are connected with its tenets; and are mutually inculcated with the art of pleasing.

A PERSON of this character grounds his motives for pleasing on the most selfish principle —He is polite, not for the honour of obliging you, as he endeavours to make you believe, but that he himself might be obliged. Suspect him, therefore, of insincerity and treachery, who sacrifices truth to complaisance, and advises you to the pursuit of an object, which would tend to his advantage.

ALWAYS distinguish the man of sense from the coxcomb. Mr. *Worthy* is possessed of a good understanding, and an exact judgment. If you are united with him, let it be the study of your life to preserve his love and esteem. His amiable character is adorned with modesty and a disposition to virtue and sobriety. I never anticipate your future happiness, but I contemplate this part of his character with pleasure. But remember the fidelity of a wife alone, will not always secure the esteem of a husband; when her personal attractions do not continue to delight his eye, she will flatter his judgment. I think you are enabled to perform this, because you are solicitous to supply your mind with those amiable qualities which are more durable than beauty. When you are no longer surrounded with a flattering circle of young men, and the world shall cease to call you beautiful, your company will be courted by men of sense, who know the value of your conversation.

I AM pleased with the conduct of some agreeable girls, and the return of civility and attention they often make to the conceited compliments of a certain class of beaux. These ladies wisely consider them as the butterflies of a day, and therefore generally scorn *to break them on a wheel!*

WHEN you are in company, where the vain and thoughtless endeavour to shew their ingenuity by ridiculing particular orders of men, your prudence will dictate to you not to countenance their abuse—The book I have just mentioned, intimates, that "there are a great many things done and said in company which a woman of virtue will neither see nor hear."— To discountenance levity, is a sure way to guard against the encroachment of temptation; to participate in the mirth of a buffoon, is to render yourself equally ridiculous. We owe to ourselves a *detestation* of folly, and to the world, the appearance of it. I would have you avoid coquetry and affectation, and the observance of my maxims will never make you a prude— Pretend, therefore, should a vain youth throw out illiberal sarcasms against Mechanicks, Lawyers, Ministers, Virtue, Religion, or any serious subject, not to comprehend the point of his wit.

I HAVE seldom spoken to you on the importance of Religion, and the veneration due to the characters of the Clergy. I always supposed your good sense capable of suggesting their necessity and eligibility. The Ministers of no nation are more remarkable for learning and piety than those of this country. The fool may pretend to scorn, and the irreligious to contemn, but every person of sense and reflection must admire that sacred order, whose business is to inform the understanding, and regulate the passions of mankind. Surely, therefore, that class of men, will continue to merit our esteem and affection, while virtue remains upon earth.

I AM always pleased with the reasonable and amiable light in which the Clergy are placed by the author of the *Guardian*—"The light," says he, "in which these points should be exposed to the view of one who is prejudiced against the names, *Religion, Church, Priest,* or the like, is to consider the Clergy as so many Philosophers, the Churches as Schools, and their Sermons as Lectures for the improvement and information of the audience. How would the heart of *Tully* or *Socrates* have rejoiced, had they lived in a nation where the law had made provision for philosophers to read lectures of philosophy, every seventh day, in several thousands of schools, erected at the publick charge, throughout the whole country, at which lectures, all ranks and sexes, without distinction, were obliged to be present, for their general improvement?"

YOU may, perhaps, think this letter too serious, but remember that virtue and religion are the foundation of education.

Adieu!

LETTER XXX.

Mrs. H O L M E S *to* M Y R A.

BELLEVIEW.

Y OU will observe, my dear friend, that most of the letters I have written to you of late, on female education, are confined to the subject of study. I am sensible of the ridicule sometimes levelled at those who are called learned ladies. Either these ladies must be uncommonly pedantick, or those who ridicule

[93]

them, uncommonly ignorant—Do not be apprehensive of acquiring that title, or sharing the ridicule, but remember that the knowledge which I wish you to acquire, is necessary to adorn your many virtues and amiable qualifications. This ridicule is evidently a *transatlantick* idea, and must have been imbibed from the source of some *English* Novel or Magazine —The *American* ladies of this class, who come within our knowledge, we know to be justly celebrated as ornaments to society, and an honour to the sex. When it is considered how many of our countrywomen are capable of the task, it is a matter of regret that *American* literature boasts so few productions from the pens of the ladies.

SELF complacency is a most necessary acquirement—for the value of a woman will always be commensurate to the opinion she entertains of herself. A celebrated *European* wit, in a letter to a lady, concenters much good advice in one short rule of conduct: "REVERENCE THYSELF."

I WAS this morning reading *Swift's* letter to a very young lady, on her marriage. Although this famous writer is not celebrated for delicacy or respect towards us, yet I wish some of his observations contained less truth—If you are in company, says this writer, when the conver-

sation turns on the manners and customs of
remote nations, or on books in verse or prose,
or on the nature and limits of virtue and vice,
it is a shame for a lady not to relish such dis-
courses, not to improve by them, and endeavour
by reading and information, to have her share
in those entertainments, rather than turn aside,
as is the usual custom, and consult with the
woman who sits next her, about a new cargo
of fans.

HE then descends to particulars, and insists
on the necessity of orthography. Is it not a
little hard, continues he, that not one gentleman's daughter in a thousand should be brought
to read or understand her own natural tongue,
or be judge of the easiest books that are written
in it; as any one may find, who can have the
patience to hear them mangle a Play or a
Novel?

IF there be any of your acquaintance to whom
this passage is applicable, I hope you will recommend the study of Mr. *Webster*'s Gram-
matical Institute, as the best work in our language to facilitate the knowledge of Grammar.
I cannot but think Mr. *Webster* intended his
valuable book for the benefit of his countrywomen: For while he delivers his *rules* in a
pure, precise, and elegant style, he *explains* his
meaning by *examples* which are calculated to

inspire the female mind with a thirst for emulation, and a desire of virtue.

NO subject has been more exhausted than that of education. Many *Utopian* schemes have been delineated, and much speculation employed. When I peruse these labours, and am persuaded the intention of their authors is to promote our welfare, I feel myself prompted to a prudent and amiable demeanour; and I suppose every woman of reason and reflection feels the same inclination to virtue, and the same sensations of gratitude, in reading the works of those writers, the characteristicks of whom, are sentiment, morality and benevolence.

WHAT books do you read, my dear? We are now finishing *Barlow's* Vision of *Columbus,* and shall begin upon *Dwight's* Conquest of *Canaan* in a few days. It is very agreeable to read with one, who points out the beauties of the author as we proceed. Such an one is *Worthy.*—Sometimes Mr. *Holmes* makes one of our party, and his notes and references to the ancient poets are very entertaining. *Worthy* is delighted with the ease and freedom with which we live here. We have little concerts, we walk, we ride, we read, we have good company —this is *Belleview* in all its glory!

ADIEU, my dear—I shall continue this subject no longer, though I flatter myself you would receive my hints with satisfaction, because you must be persuaded I love you, and so interest myself in your welfare—I need not add that I think your conduct worthy of you. You are such a good girl that I know not in what to direct you; for you leave me no room for advice —continue to anticipate the desires of my heart, and to secure the high opinion you have there obtained.

Your friend forever!

LETTER XXXI.

Mrs. HOLMES *to* MYRA.

BELLEVIEW.

IF the affair of your brother and *Harriot* be serious, and matrimony is really on the tapis, do not fail to make me *previously* acquainted with it——I very much doubt the evidence of the verses—they weigh little in my mind—and he is easily excused for sending them to so fine a girl as *Harriot*.

YOUR observations on her dependence on Mrs. *Francis* do honour to your heart—virtue

does not consist in affluence and independence
—nor can it be reflected on us by the glory of
our connexions—those who pride themselves
on it, make but an indifferent figure; for in the
estimation of all sensible people—true merit is
personal.

HOWEVER, my dear friend, as one who wishes
for your welfare and the happiness of your
family, I advise you to discourage the proposed
connexion—and if you cannot undertake this
disagreeable task with a *certainty of success,*
do not fail to acquaint me of it *speedily.*

Adieu!

LETTER XXXII.

HARRINGTON *to* WORTHY.

BOSTON.

W HAT ails my heart? I feel a void
here—and yet I verge towards my happiness—
for a few days makes *Harriot* mine—*Myra*
says I had *better not marry her.* What could
prompt her to use such an expression? *Better*

not marry her. She has repeated it several times
—and with too much eagerness—I give no heed
to it—and yet why should it affect me in this
manner? Is it an artifice to fathom the depth
of my love? Such schemes are my utter aversion—it disturbs me—I hate such artifice—
You cannot imagine how it touches my heart.

Adieu!

LETTER XXXIII.

Mrs. HOLMES *to* MYRA.

BELLEVIEW.

IT is the duty of friends to be interested in all the concerns of one another—to
join in their joys and to avert the stroke of
danger. It is the duty of a centinel to give the
alarm at the approach of what he may think
such—and if the result does not prove to be
a real evil—he has but performed his duty, and
the action is meritorious.

IF your exertions to countermine the connexion of your brother with *Harriot* should

prove ineffectual (and do not fail to acquaint me with it either way) I HAVE A TALE TO UN-FOLD which may possibly forbid the bans.

LETTER XXXIV.

HARRINGTON *to* WORTHY.

BOSTON.

I FIND my temper grow extremely irritable—my sensibility is wounded at the slightest neglect—I am very tenacious of every thing, and of every body.

A PARTY was made yesterday to go on the water; I was omitted, and the neglect hurt me. I inquired the cause, and what think you is the answer? "I am no company—I am asked a question and return nothing to the point—I am absent—I am strangely altered within a few days—I am thinking of a different subject when I ought to be employed in conversation—I am extravagant in my observations—I am no company."

THEY would persuade me that I am little better than a mad man—I have no patience with their nonsensical replies—Such wiseacres do not deserve my pity.

Farewel!

LETTER XXXV.

MYRA *to* Mrs. HOLMES.

BOSTON.

Y OUR letter is filled with such ambiguous expressions, that I am utterly at a loss to discover your meaning.

I HAVE, however, sounded him on the article of marriage, and the result is—he loves *Harriot* most passionately—and on account of my father's aversion to early marriages, will marry her privately in a few days.

THE oftener I read your letter, the more I am perplexed and astonished: "YOU HAVE A TALE TO UNFOLD"—For Heaven's sake then unfold it, before it be too late—and as you dread the consequence of keeping it secret, by disclosing it to me, you will prevent the mischief, you so much deprecate——I am all impatience.

Adieu!

LETTER XXXVI.

HARRINGTON *to* WORTHY.

BOSTON.

I HAVE just left *Harriot*—but how have I left her? In tears. I wish I had not gone. Mrs. *Francis* had intrusted *Harriot* with some trifling commission—It was not done—she had not had time to perform it. *Harriot* was reprimanded——Yes! by Heaven—this Mrs. *Francis* had the insolence to reprimand *Harriot* in my presence—I was mortified—I walked to the window—my heart was on fire—my blood boiled in my veins—it is impossible to form an idea of the disorder of my nerves—*Harriot's* were equally agitated—Mrs. *Francis* saw our confusion and retired—she left me so completely out of temper that I was forced to follow her example. I kissed away the tear from the cheek of *Harriot* and withdrew to my chamber.

HERE let me forget what has passed—my irritability will not permit it—my feelings are too easily set in motion to enjoy long quietness—my nerves are delicately strung; they are now out of tune, and it is a hard matter to harmonize them.

I FEEL *that I have a soul*—and every man of sensibility feels it within himself. I will relate a circumstance I met with in my late travels through *Southcarolina*—I was always susceptible of *touches of nature.*

I HAD often remarked a female slave pass by my window to a spring to fetch water. She had something in her air superiour to those of her situation—a fire that the damps of slavery had not extinguished.

AS I was one day walking behind her, the wind blew her tattered handkerchief from her neck and exposed it to my sight—I asked her the cause of the scar on her shoulder—She answered composedly, and with an earnestness that proved she was not ashamed to declare it—"It is the mark of the whip," said she, and went on with the history of it, without my desiring her to proceed—"my boy, of about ten years old, was unlucky enough to break a glass tumbler—this crime was immediately inquired into—I trembled for the fate of my child, and was thought to be guilty. I did not deny the charge, and was tied up. My former good character availed nothing. Under every affliction, we may receive consolation; and during the smart of the whip, I rejoiced—because I shielded with my body the lash from my child; and I rendered thanks to the best of beings that I was allowed to suffer for him."

[103]

"HEROICALLY spoken!" said I, "may he whom you call the best of beings continue you in the same sentiments—may thy soul be ever disposed to SYMPATHIZE with thy children, and with thy brethren and sisters in calamity—then shalt thou feel every circumstance of thy life afford thee satisfaction; and repining and melancholy shall fly from thy bosom—all thy labours will become easy—all thy burdens light, and the yoke of slavery will never gall thy neck."

I WAS sensibly relieved as I pronounced these words, and I felt my heart glow with feelings of exquisite delight, as I anticipated the happy time when the sighs of the slave shall no longer expire in the air of freedom. What delightful sensations are those in which the heart is interested! In which it stoops to enter into the little concerns of the most remote ramification of Nature! Let the vain, the giddy, and the proud pass on without deigning to notice them—let them cheat themselves of happiness—these are circumstances which are important only to a sentimental traveller.

HAIL *Sensibility!* Sweetener of the joys of life! Heaven has implanted thee in the breasts of his children—to soothe the sorrows of the afflicted—to mitigate the wounds of the stranger who falleth in our way. *Thou* regardest with an eye of pity, those whom *wealth* and *ambition* treat in terms of reproach. Away, ye seekers of power—ye boasters of wealth—ye are the *Levite* and the *Pharisee,* who restrain the hand of charity from the indigent, and turn with indignation from the way-worn son of misery: —But *Sensibility* is the good *Samaritan,* who taketh him by the hand, and consoleth him, and poureth wine and oil into his wounds. Thou art a pleasant companion—a grateful friend—and a *neighbour* to those who are destitute of shelter.——

FROM thee! Author of Nature! from thee, thou inexhaustible spring of love supreme, floweth this tide of affection and SYMPATHY—thou whose tender care extendeth to the least of thy creation—and whose eye is not inattentive even though a sparrow fall to the ground.

LETTER XXXVII.

Mrs. HOLMES *to* MYRA.

BELLEVIEW, 12 *o'clock at night.*

I CANNOT rest——this affair lies so heavy on my mind, that sleep flies from my eye-lids. Your brother *must* discontinue his addresses to *Harriot*——with what should I not have to upbraid myself, if, through my remissness—your brother marries his sister!

GREAT God! of what materials hast thou compounded the hearts of thy creatures! admire, O my friend! the operation of NATURE—and the power of SYMPATHY!——

HARRIOT IS YOUR SISTER! I dispatch the bearer at this late hour to confide in your bosom the important secret.

Adieu!

LETTER XXXVIII.

MYRA *to* Mrs. HOLMES.

BOSTON.

ACCEPT my warmest acknowledgment, my good friend, for your kindness— Your letter sufficiently explains your former anxiety—it has removed all ambiguities.

YOUR servant entered hastily with the letter —and gave it me with evident tokens of its containing a matter of importance.—My father was present—I broke it open, not without agita-

tion—I read it—but the shock was too severe—
it fell from my hands, and I sunk into the chair.

MY fainting was not of any duration. I
opened my eyes and found my father supporting me—but the idea of *Harriot* was still en-
graven deeply in my heart—I inquired for my
sister—the tear rolled down his cheek—it was
a sufficient answer to my inquiry—He said
nothing—there was no necessity of his saying
a word.

COULD I ask him to explain your letter? No—
my heart anticipated his feelings—the impropriety struck me at once. *"You have a tale to
unfold."* Do not delay to unfold it.

Adieu!

LETTER XXXIX.

Mrs. HOLMES *to* MYRA.

BELLEVIEW.

I READILY undertake to give you a
sketch of the history of *Harriot*. Her mother's
name was *Maria Fawcet;* her person I yet recollect, and forgive me if I drop a tear of pity
at the recital of her misfortunes.

[107]

MY mother and Mrs. *Holmes* were remarkable friends, and the intimacy, you know, was maintained between the two families. I was on a visit with my mother when the destiny of *Maria* led her to *Belleview*. I was frequently there during her illness—and was with her in her last moments.

IT was the custom of Mrs. *Holmes* to walk in the garden towards the close of the day. She was once indulging her usual walk, when she was alarmed by the complaints of a woman which came from the road. Pity and humanity were ever peculiar characteristicks of my amiable parent—She hastened to the place from whence the sound issued, and beheld a young woman, bathed in tears, sitting upon the ground. She inquired the cause of her distress, with that eager solicitude to relieve, which a sight so uncommon would naturally occasion. It was sometime before the distressed woman could return an intelligible answer, and then she with difficulty proceeded: "Your goodness, Madam, is unmerited—you behold a stranger, without home—without friends—and whose misery bears her down to an untimely grave— Life, truly is a blessing—but my life is become burthensome, and were the Almighty this moment to command me to the world of spirits, methinks I could gladly obey the summons, and rejoice in the stroke which bade me depart from sorrow and the world." "Moderate your grief, my dear woman, repine not at the will of Providence, nor suffer yourself to despair, however severe your misfortunes."

THE unfortunate woman was at length prevailed on to accompany Mrs. *Holmes* into the house, she partook of some refreshment and retired to sleep. In a few days she appeared to be better; but it was a temporary recovery; she then told her story, with frequent interruptions, in substance as follows:——

History of Maria.

"I DATE the rise of my misfortunes," said *Maria,* "at the beginning of my acquaintance with the Honourable Mr. *Harrington.*—But for his solicitations I might still have lived in peace—a sister would not have had occasion to blush at the sound of my name—nor had a mother's pillow been steeped in tears, too fondly prone to remember a graceless but repenting child—We lived happily together in the days of my father, but when it pleased Providence to remove him, we no longer asserted our pretentions to that rank of life which our straitened finances were unable to continue—A young woman in no eligible circumstances, has much to apprehend from the solicitations of a man of affluence. I am now better persuaded of this truth, than I ever was before—for this was my unhappy situation—I always entertained a predilection for Mr. *Harrington*—he urged his passion with protestations of sincerity and affection—he found my heart too slightly guarded—he strove—he triumphed.

"——MUST I proceed!——

"A SMILING female was the offspring of our illicit connexion——Ah! my little *Harriot!*" continued *Maria,* as she wiped away a tear from her eye, "mayest thou enjoy that happiness which is denied to thy mother.

"OUR amour was not fated to last long—I discovered his gay temper to be materially altered—he was oftentimes thoughtful and melancholy, and his visits became suddenly shorter, and less frequent.

"I AFTERWARDS thought this change of conduct owing to jealousy—for he once asked me if a gentleman had called upon me—I persisted in avowing my abhorrence of his ungenerous suspicion—He left me abruptly, and I saw nothing of him after.

"A STROKE so unexpected fell heavy on my heart—it awakened me to the state of misery into which my imprudence had hurried me.— What recompense could I expect from my Se-

ducer?—He had been married two years—
From the inflexibility of his temper I had little
to hope, and I formed a determination of leaving town, for I had now indubitable testimony
of his affection being estranged from me—half
frantick, I immediately set out—but whither I
knew not—I walked with precipitation until
Providence directed me to your hospitable door:
To your goodness, Madam, I am indebted for
prolonging my existence a *few days:* For
amidst the kindness and civilities of those
around me, I feel myself rapidly verging towards the grave. I prepare myself for my approaching fate—and daily wait the stroke of
death with trembling expectation."

SHE wrote to Mr. *Harrington* about a
week before her decease—I transcribe the
Letter:——

"The Hon. Mr. HARRINGTON.

"TO the man for whom my bleeding heart
yet retains its wonted affection, though the
author of my guilt and misery, do I address
my feeble complaint—O! *Harrington,* I am
verging to a long eternity—and it is with difficulty I support myself while my trembling
hand traces the dictates of my heart. Indisposed

[111]

as I am—and unable as I feel to prosecute this task—I however collect all my powers to bid you a long—a final farewel.

"oh! *Harrington,* I am about to depart—for why should I tarry here? In bitter tears of sorrow do I weep away the night, and the returning day but augments the anguish of my heart, by recalling to view the sad sight of my misfortunes. And have I not cause for this severe anguish, at once the sorrow and disgrace of my family?—Alas! my poor mother!—Death shall expiate the crime of thy daughter, nor longer raise the blush of indignation on thy glowing cheek.—Ought I not, therefore, to welcome the hand of death?

"but what will become of my poor helpless infant, when its mother lies forgotten in the grave? Wilt thou direct its feet in the path of virtue and rectitude?—Wilt thou shelter it from the rude blasts of penury and want?—Open your heart to the solicitude of a mother—of a mother agonizing for the future welfare of her child. Let me intreat you to perform this request—by the love which you professed for thy *Maria*—by her life which you have sacrificed.

"and wilt thou not drop a tear of pity in the grave of thy *Maria?*—I know thy soul is a soul of sensibility; but my departure shall not grieve thee—no, my *Harrington,* it shall not wrest a sigh from thy bosom—rather let me live, and defy the malice and misery of the world—But can tenderness—can love atone for the sacrifices I have made?—Will it blot out my errours from the book of memory? Will love be an excuse for my crime, or hide me from the eye of the malignant—No, my *Harrington,* it will not. The passion is unwarrantable. Be it thine, gentle *Amelia*—be it thine to check the obtruding sigh, and wipe away the tear from his face —for thou art his wife, and thy soul is the seat of compassion—But—for me——

"Farewel—farewel forever!

MARIA."

SHE survived but a short time—and frequently expressed a concern for her child—but Mrs. *Holmes* quieted her fears by promising to protect it. She accordingly made inquiry after it—and it is the same *Harriot* who was educated by her order, and whom she afterwards placed in the family of Mrs. *Francis.*

THE assurances of my mother were like balm to the broken hearted *Maria*—"I shall now," said she, "die in peace."

THE following is a copy of a letter written by the Rev. Mr. *Holmes* to the Hon. Mr. *Harrington:*——

"BELLEVIEW.

"SIR,

"WE have a scene of distress at our house peculiarly pathetick and affecting, and of which you, perhaps, are the sole author—You have had a criminal connexion with Miss *Fawcet*— you have turned her upon the world inhumanly —but chance—rather let me say Providence, hath directed her footsteps to my dwelling, where she is kindly entertained, and will be so, as long as she remains in this wilderness world, which is to be, I fear, but a short time—And shall she not, though she hath been decoyed from the road that leadeth to peace, long life and happiness—shall she not, if she return with tears of repentance and contrition, be entitled to our love and charity? Yes—this is my doctrine—If I behold any child of human nature distressed and forlorn, and in real want of the necessities of life, must I restrain or withhold the hand of charity—must I cease to recal the departing spirit of them that are ready to perish, until I make diligent inquiry into their circumstances and character? Surely, my friend, it is a duty incumbent on us by the ties of humanity and fellow feeling, and by the duty imposed on us by our holy religion, equally to extend the hand of relief to *all the necessitous*— however they may be circumstanced in the great family of mankind.

"THE crime of *Maria* is not the blackest in the annals of human turpitude; but however guilty she might have been, the tears of penitence do certainly make atonement therefor.

"THUS much have I thought proper to say in vindication of my conduct—in sheltering under my roof a poor wanderer—who hath strayed, but not wantonly, and who hath now happily returned.

"ONE would imagine, there was little necessity of making such a vindication to you; but my sentiments always flow from the abundance of my heart, and I am willing the whole world should judge of those which influence my conduct——Now, though some men, whose charity is contracted, and who may be denominated *prudes in virtue,* might deem wrongfully of my attention to the calamity of this frail woman— yet let me appeal to the hearts and understandings of all men, and these in particular, if I have erred, whether it be not an errour on the side of humanity. Would to God such amiable errours were more frequent!—In as much, my friend, as there is joy in heaven over one sin-

ner that repenteth, I may say with assurance
that I have felt an emanation of this heavenly
joy animate my heart, in beholding this woman
delighting to steer her course heavenward.

"FROM the unhappy condition of *Maria,* I
have been led to reflect on the mischievous tendency of SEDUCTION. Methinks I view the
distressing picture in all its horrid colours.——

"BEHOLD the youthful virgin arrayed in all
the delightful charms of vivacity, modesty and
sprightliness—Behold even while she is rising
in beauty and dignity, like a lily of the valley,
in the full blossom of her graces, she is cut off
suddenly by the rude hand of the Seducer. Un-
acquainted with his baseness and treachery,
and too ready to repose confidence in him—
she is deluded by the promises and flattery of
the man who professes the greatest love and
tenderness for her welfare:—But did she
understand the secret villainy of his intentions
—would she appear thus elate and joyous?
Would she assent to her ruin? Would she sub-
scribe her name to the catalogue of infamy?
Would she kiss the hand of the atrocious
dastard, already raised to give the final wound
to her reputation and peace?

"O! WHY is there not an adequate punishment for this crime, when that of a common

traitor is marked with its deserved iniquity and abhorrence!

"IS it necessary to depicture the state of this deluded young creature after her fall from virtue? Stung with remorse, and frantick with despair, does she not fly from the face of day, and secrete her conscious head in the bosom of eternal forgetfulness? Melancholy and guilt transfix her heart, and she sighs out her miserable existence—the prey of poverty, ignominy and reproach! Lost to the world, to her friends, and to herself, she blesses the approach of death in whatever shape he may appear, that terminates a life, no longer a blessing to its possessour, or a joy to those around her.

"BEHOLD her stretched upon the mournful bier!—Behold her silently descend to the grave! —Soon the wild weeds spring afresh round the *little hillock,* as if to shelter the remains of betrayed innocence—and the friends of her youth shun even the spot which conceals her relicks.

"SUCH is the consequence of SEDUCTION, but it is not the only consequence. Peace and happiness fly the nuptial couch which is unattended by love and fidelity. The mind no longer enjoys its quiet, while it ceases to cherish sentiments of truth and gratitude. The sacred *ties* of connubial duty are not to be violated with impunity; for though a violation of those *ties* may be overlooked by the eye of justice, the heart shall supply a *monitor,* who will not fail to correct those, who are hardy enough to burst them asunder.——I am, &c.

"W. HOLMES."

TO this Letter, Mr. *Harrington* returned the following Answer.

Hon. Mr. HARRINGTON *to the* Rev. Mr. HOLMES.

"PERMIT me, my ever honoured friend, to return you thanks for your late favours—need I add—an acknowledgment for your liberality? No—your heart supplies a source of pleasure which is contantly nourished by your goodness and universal charity.——

"THE picture you have exhibited of a ruined female is undoubtedly just, but that the *rude spoiler* has his share of remorse is equally so— The conclusion of your letter is a real picture of the situation of my heart.

"PERHAPS you was always ignorant of the real motives that influenced me, and gave a particular bias to my conduct—At an early period of my life, I adopted a maxim, that *the most necessary learning was a knowledge of the world,* the pursuit of which, quadrating with a volatility of disposition, presented a variety of scenes to my heated imagination. The *eclat* of my companions gratifying my vanity and increasing the gale of passion, I became insensibly hurried down the stream of dissipation. Here I saw mankind in every point of view—from the acme of the most consummate refinement, to the most abject stage of degradation. I soon became a ready proficient in the great school of the world—but an alteration of conduct was soon after necessary—I was compelled to it, not so much from the world's abhorrence of a dissolute course of life, as the dictates of my own heart—It was, indeed, my policy to flatter the world, and exhibit a fair outside—for I was in love with *Amelia*—My licentious amour with *Maria* was secret—she was affectionate and tender—her manners were pleasing, but still I was unhappy.——

"MY career of dissipation, however alluring it struck my vitiated fancy, left little satisfaction on the mind—Reflection had its turn—and the happiness I had promised myself in a connexion with the amiable *Amelia,* I fully enjoyed in our marriage. A course of uninterrupted tranquillity ensued, but it was of short duration. The volatility of my temper, and the solicitude of my old associates, induced me at subsequent periods to fall again into my old vagaries. The taverns frequently found me engaged in meannesses derogatory to the character of a gentleman. These things I perceived affected the soul of *Amelia*—she was all meekness, gentleness and compassion, and she never once upbraided me with my illiberal conduct;

> But let concealment, like a worm in the bud,
> Feed on her damask cheek.

"BLESSED be that power who has implanted within us that consciousness of reproach, which springs from gentleness and love!—Hail sensibility! Ye eloquent *tears* of *beauty!* that add dignity to human nature by correcting its foibles—it was *these* that corrected my faults when recrimination would have failed of success—it was *these* that opened every avenue of contrition in my heart, when *words* would have dammed up every sluice of repentance.

"IT was now I appeared fully sensible that my conduct had hitherto been a course of disorder, and that systems of reformation, however well planned, had been overturned by the breath of adulation, before they had been thoroughly carried into execution—that I had been drifting upon a sea of inconsistency, without exercising my judgment; like a ship without a rudder, buffetted on the bosom of the ocean, the sport of winds and waves.

"THE criminality of my connexion with *Maria* appeared with the most aggravated circumstances; it stung me with remorse—and I instantly determined, however severe the conflict, to tear her from my bosom—to see her no more.—But how was I to inform her of it? —In what manner was I to bring about such a task?—*Maria* must be sacrificed to the happiness of *Amelia*. This was all I had to perform—it was a short lesson, but it was a hard one for me to execute.

"WITH this determination, however, I entered the apartment of *Maria*—Duty to *Amelia* and gratitude to *Maria* interchangeably agitated me—the contention was dubious—but duty prevailed, and I adhered to my former resolution—yet how was I to tell her *this would be the last visit?*—Conscious she had ever acted in conformity to my wishes—how could I accuse her, without accusing myself?—I threw out a few inconsiderate, and ungrateful hints of jealousy, and left the room abruptly. The feelings of *Maria* must have been injured—but however her sensibility was affected, mine was doubly so; I felt for her—I felt for our infant, and these feelings were added to the afflictions which had already burst upon my devoted head. A few days consideration, however, convinced me of the impropriety and ingratitude of my behaviour to *Maria*—I hastened to tell her of it—to place her in a situation that should screen her from penury and malice—and to make provision for the child—but, she was not to be found. I was informed that she had suddenly disappeared, and that a countryman had, by her order, called and taken away the child but a few hours before. This information burst upon my head like the voice of sudden thunder —I stood motionless, but my agitation was too violent to be of any long duration.——

A natural tear I shed, but wip'd it soon.

"IT was your goodness, and the humanity of your family, that sheltered the wretched *Maria,* and provided for the helpless *Harriot*—Your feelings are your reward.

"FROM all the variegated scenes of my past life, I daily learn some new lesson of humanity. Experience hath been my tutor—I now take a retrospect of my past conduct with delibera-

tion, but not without some serious reflection:
Like a sailor, escaped from shipwreck, who sits
safely on the shore and views the horrours of
the tempest; but as the gale subsides, and the
waves hide their heads in the bosom of the
deep, he beholds with greater concern the mischief of the storm, and the dangers he hath
escaped. From what innate principle does this
arise, but from the *God within the mind!*—I
assert it for the honour of human nature, that
no man, however dissolute, but comes back to
the hour of reflection and solemn thoughtfulness—when the actions that are passed return
upon the mind, and this *internal monitor* sits
in judgment upon them, and gives her verdict
of approbation or dislike.

"HE who listens to its call, views his character in its proper light—I have attended to
its cry, and I see my deformity—I recal my
mispent time, but in vain—I reflect on the
misery of *Maria,* and I curse my temerity—I
reflect on the state into which I have plunged
a once happy female, and am eager to apply a
speedy remedy, but this is vain also: Can I
restore her that virtue—that innocence—that
peace, of which I have unmanfully robbed her?
——Let us leave the melancholy subject.——

"I WILL not so far supersede the fruit of
your benevolence, as to presume to offer you

[123]

any other recompense, than my sincere prayers
for your happiness.

    "I have the honour to be,

      "With respect,

        "Your &c.

         "J. HARRINGTON."

THE disorder of *Maria* was fatal and rapid—
but I hasten to the last scene of her life—it has,
though I was young, made an impression on
my mind that time cannot efface. I went to her,
as she was seated on the bed—virtue and harmony were blended in her aspect—she was
serene and composed—and her mien, while it
expressed a consciousness of superiour worth
and dignity, exhibited in one view, a striking
picture of the grandeur of the human soul—
patient, though afflicted—of a spirit broken,
and borne down by severe distress, yet striving
to surmount all, and aspire to heaven. In what
words shall I paint to you, my dear *Myra*, her
heroism and greatness of mind? "Weep not
for me," said she, perceiving my emotion—
"Death has nothing shocking to me—I have
familiarized myself to his terrours—I feel the
gradual decay of mortality; and waiting with
confidence in the father of mercy, I am prepared to resign this mortal breath—I resign it

in firm assurance of the soul's blessed immor-
tality—Death I view as freeing me from a
world which has lost its relish—as opening new
scenes of happiness——But a few moments,"
continued she, clasping my hand, "and the scene
of life is closed forever—Heaven opens on my
soul—I go where all tears shall be wiped
away—I welcome death as the angel of peace."
——She uttered these words with a placid smile
of resignation—her head sunk down on the
pillow—and the next minute she was an angel.

"SOUL of the universe!" exclaimed my
father-in-law—"there flew the gentlest spirit
that ever animated human dust—Great were
thy temptations—sincere thy repentance. If
some human infirmity fell to thy lot, thy tears,
dear shade, have washed out thy guilt forever!"

LETTER XL.

Mrs. HOLMES *to* MYRA.

BELLEVIEW.

HAVING presented you with several
observations on Seduction, I think it will not
be *mal apropos* to consider the question in an-

other point of view, and discover how a woman may be accessary to her own ruin—It is hardly worth while to contend about the difference between the meaning of the terms *accessary* and *principal.* The difference, in fact, is small; but when a woman, by her imprudence, exposes herself, she is *accessary;* for though her heart may be pure, her conduct is a tacit invitation to the Seducer.

EDUCATED in the school of luxury and pride, the female heart grows gradually torpid to the fine feelings of sensibility—the blush of modesty wears off—the charms of elegant simplicity fade by degrees—and the continual hurry of dissipation, supersedes the improvement of serious reflection. Reflection is a kind of relaxation from frolicking—it encourages the progress of virtue, and upholds the heart from sinking to depravity.

WE may lay it down as a principle, that *that conduct which will bear the test of reflection, and which creates a pleasure in the mind from a consciousness of acting right, is virtuous: And she whose conduct will not bear this test, is necessarily degenerating, and she is assenting to her destruction.*

LET a lady be liberal or even magnificent, according to her circumstances or situation in life; but let the heart remain uncorrupt, let her not be contaminated by wealth, ambition or splendour. She may then take a happy retrospect of her conduct—her heart cannot upbraid her—and the suffrage of her own mind is a convincing proof that she has not strayed from the path of virtue.

HAPPY they who can thus reflect—who can recal to view the scenes that are passed, and behold their actions with reiterated satisfaction—they become ambitious of excelling in every thing virtuous, because they are certain of securing a continual reward: For as a mighty river fertilizes the country through which it passes and encreases in magnitude and force until it empty itself into the ocean: So virtue fertilizes or improves the heart, and gathers strength and vigour by continual progression, until it centre in the consummation of its desires.

DAZZLED by the glitter of splendour, and unmindful of the real charms of economy and simplicity, the female heart sighs for the enjoyment of fashion, and flutters to join the motley train of pleasure. But how is it deluded by empty deceptions! Like the fruit which sprang up in the infernal regions, beautiful to the eye, but which left upon the taste bitter ashes, and was followed by repentance—A great quantity of this kind of fruit presents itself to my rashly judging sex; and it frequently happens that their hearts have as little inclination to resist the temptation, as our general parent to refuse the fatal apple.

WE do not rouse to our aid fortitude to enable us to surmount the temptation, but yield ourselves to a kind of voluntary slavery. Hence it is observable, that a woman is often unhappy in the midst of pleasures—and petulent without cause—that she is trifling in matters of the highest importance; and the most momentous concern is considered futile, as whim and caprice may chance to dictate.

THE progress of female luxury, however slow it may appear, unless timely checked, works with infallible and destructive advances. The rule we at first adopted might perhaps answer this check; for by the examination there recommended, we behold the dangers of a continuation of such conduct—Ruin and contempt, the invariable concommitants of vice and immorality, proclaim their denunciations on a prosecution of it.

LET us examine the gradual steps, and the consequence of female luxury.—A desire to be admired is the first. Behold a woman surrounded by her worshippers, receiving the sacrifice of adulation—what was given her at first as compliment, she now demands as her due. She finds herself disappointed, and is mortified. The first desire still predominating, she attaches herself to the votaries of pride, who direct their feet in the paths of extravagance and irreligion. Thus sunk into effeminacy and meanness, *she forfeits her virtue rather than her pride.* Thus terminates the career of a woman, whose mind is debilitated, and whose life is expended in the pursuit of vanity.

IT is said of some species of *American* serpents, that they have the power of charming birds and small animals, which they destine for their prey. The serpent is stretched underneath a tree—it looks stedfastly on the bird—their eyes meet to separate no more—the charm begins to operate—the fascinated bird flutters and hops from limb to limb, till unable any longer to extend its wings, it falls into the voracious jaws of its enemy: This is no ill emblem of the fascinating power of pleasure. Surrounded with temptation, and embarrassed in her circumstances, a woman of dissipation becomes less tenacious of her honour—and falls an easy prey to the fascinating power of the SEDUCER.

HAVING traced to you, my dear *Myra,* the rise, advancement and termination of pleasure and pride in the female heart, it appears almost unnecessary to remark that this conduct cannot bear the test of reflection and serious examination. We may, however, observe on the contrary, that a woman who advances a few steps, often hurries on still further to prevent thought. This bars the way to a return to that conduct which *can* give pleasure on recollection. She behaves to herself as the populace did formerly to women suspected of witchcraft—they were tied neck and heels and thrown into the river; if they swam they were hung for witches—if they sank they were acquitted of the crime, but drowned in the experiment: So when we only suspect our hearts of an errour, we plunge still deeper into the sea of dissipation, to prevent the trial of that conduct which impartial reason and judgment would approve.

NOTWITHSTANDING I give this instance as an encouragement for virtue; yet in all those I have mentioned is a woman *accessary* to her ruin.

DO not imagine, my dear *Myra,* that I mean to argue against all pleasure—Many of us set out on a principle of false delicacy and destructive rivalship; we cannot behold a fine woman without wishing to appear finer. A laudable emulation in the conduct of all women is extremely praiseworthy—it stimulates them in the line of their duty—increases vivacity and good humour; and ambition, thus directed and pursued, I beg leave to designate a female virtue, because it is productive of the most happy consequences.

BUT it sometimes happens that particular virtues loose themselves in their neighbouring vices, and this laudable emulation degenerates into destructive rivalship.

A GENTEEL, handsome woman, deservedly shares the esteem and admiration of all men; but why should this esteem and admiration, justly paid to merit, give us disquiet? the answer is ready. That desire to be admired, so predominant in all females, by degrees works itself into the ruling passion, and precludes from the mind the particular virtue of emulation; for why a woman who merits the love of the world, should draw on her the disapprobation of many of her own sex, can be accounted for, by no other principle, than the mean, pitiful passion of envy.

THIS may possibly give rise to defamation. It is astonishing how this practice prevails among a *few* persons—because it is known by experience, to prove subversive of its very intention.—The arrows of envy recoil upon herself.

HOW foolish must that woman appear who depreciates the merit of another, that she may appear unrivalled! She raises up the dykes of ill nature, and inundates the land with a flood of scandal, but unhappily drowns herself in the event.

I LEAVE it to the result of your observation,

my dear *Myra,* whether the woman who is first
to develope her stores of defamation, and
through false emulation, the first to traduce a
woman of real merit and virtue, is not also the
first who becomes a scandal to herself, and
consequently the first that is contemned.

HOW opposite are the pursuits and rewards
of her who participates in every rational enjoyment of life, without mixing in those scenes of
indiscretion which give pain on recollection!—
Whose chymical genius leads her to extract the
poison from the most luxuriant flowers, and
to draw honey even from the weeds of society.
She mixes with the world seemingly indis-
criminately—and because she would secure to
herself that satisfaction which arises from a
consciousness of acting right, she views her
conduct with an eye of scrutiny. Though her
temper is free and unrestrained, her heart is
previously secured by the precepts of prudence
—for prudence is but another name for virtue.
Her manners are unruffled, and her disposition
calm, temperate and dispassionate, however she
may be surrounded by the temptations of the
world.

Adieu!

LETTER XLI.

HARRINGTON *to* WORTHY.

BOSTON.

PRAY that the sun of Thursday may rise propitious—that it may gild the face of nature with joy. It is the day that beholds thy friend united in the indissoluble bands of *Hymen.*

Let this auspicious day be ever sacred,
No mourning, no misfortune happen on it;
Let it be marked for triumphs and rejoicings,
Let happy lovers ever keep it holy,
Choose it to bless their hopes and crown their
    wishes.

IT is the day that gives me *Harriot* forever.

Adieu!

LETTER XLII.

The Hon. Mr. HARRINGTON
to the Rev. Mr. HOLMES.

BOSTON.

YOU very well know of my amour
with *Maria,* and that a daughter was the offspring of that illicit connexion—That sixteen
years have elapsed since, by your goodness, she
has lived with Mrs. *Francis,* and let me add,
daily improving in beauty and every amiable
accomplishment—But how shall we be able—
how shall we pretend to investigate the great
springs by which we are actuated, or account
for the operation of SYMPATHY—my son, who
has been at home about eight weeks, has acci-
dentally seen her, and to complete THE TRI-
UMPH OF NATURE—has loved her. He is now
even upon the point of marrying—shall I proceed!—*of marrying his Sister!*—A circumstance seemingly fortuitous has discovered this
important affair—I fly to prevent incest—Do
not upbraid me with being the author of my
own misfortunes.—"This comes of your liber-

[134]

tinism," you will say, "this comes of your adultery!"——Spare your reflections, my friend—my heart is monitor enough—I am strangely agitated!

Adieu!

LETTER XLIII.

The Hon. Mr. HARRINGTON
to the Rev. Mr. HOLMES.

BOSTON.

MY heart failed me! twenty times have I attempted to break the matter to my son—and twenty times have I returned from the task—I have engaged a friend to acquaint him how nearly connected he already is with the object of his love. This is a new, and to me a sorrowful instance of the force of SYMPATHY —My grief is insupportable—my affliction is greater than I can bear—it will bring down my grey hairs with sorrow to the grave.

Farewel!

LETTER XLIV.

HARRINGTON *to* WORTHY.

BOSTON.

ALL my airy schemes of love and happiness are vanished like a dream. Read this, and pity your unfortunate friend.

To Mr. T. HARRINGTON.

"SIR,

"YOU are about to marry a young lady of great beauty and accomplishments—I beg you to bestow a few serious thoughts on this important business—Let me claim your attention, while I disclose an affair, which materially concerns you—*Harriot* must not be your wife— You know your father is averse to your early connecting yourself in marriage with any woman—The duty we owe a parent is sacred, but this is not the only barrier to your marriage—the ties of consanguinity prevent it—

[136]

She is your SISTER——Your father, or Miss *Harrington,* will inform you more particularly —It is sufficient for me to have hinted it in time.——I am, with the most perfect esteem, and sincere wishes for your happiness, your

"UNKNOWN FRIEND, &c."

(IN CONTINUATION.)

THE gloom of melancholy in the faces of the family but too well corroborated this intelligence—so I asked no questions—they read in my countenance that I had received the letter, and my sister put into my hand *The History of Maria*—I concealed my emotion while I read the account—"It is a pitiful tale," said I, as I returned it—and walked out of the room to give vent to the agitation of my heart.

I HAVE not yet seen *Harriot*—*Myra* has run to greet her with the new title of *sister*. Adieu! my friend—little happiness is left for me in this world.

LETTER XLV.

MYRA *to Mrs.* HOLMES.

BOSTON.

IN what words shall I describe to you, my dear friend, the misery that has suddenly overwhelmed us! It is impossible to communicate the distressed situation of *Harriot*—Expression is inadequate to give you an idea of our meeting—I called her my friend—my sister —She always loved me—but joy and affection gave way to passion—Her speech refused its office—

> Sorrow in all its pomp was there,
> Mute and magnificent without a tear.

SHE had gained a sister—she had lost a lover —a burst of joy would suddenly break from her, but it was of short duration—and was succeeded by pangs of exquisite distress—nature was unable to support it, and she fainted under the weight of the severe conflict. Her constitution at best is feeble; her present illness is therefore attended with more danger—Unless a speedy alteration should take place, the physician has little hopes of her recovery.——Heaven preserve us!

Farewel!

———

LETTER XLVI.

HARRINGTON *to* WORTHY.

BOSTON.

I HAVE seen her—I prest her to my heart—I called her my Love—my *Sister*. Tenderness and sorrow were in her eyes—How am I guilty, my friend—How is this transport a crime? My love is the most pure, the most holy —*Harriot* beheld me with tears of the most tender affection—"Why," said she, "why, my friend, my dear *Harrington,* have I loved! but in what manner have I been culpable? HOW WAS I TO KNOW YOU WERE MY BROTHER?— Yes! I might have known it—how else could you have been so kind—so tender—so affectionate!"—Here was all the horrour of con-

[139]

flicting passions, expressed by gloomy silence—
by stifled cries—by convulsions—by sudden
floods of tears—The scene was too much for
my heart to bear—I bade her adieu—my heart
was breaking—I tore myself from her and
retired.

WHAT is human happiness? The prize for
which all strive, and so few obtain; the more
eagerly we pursue it, the farther we stray from
the object: Wherefore I have determined
within myself that we increase in misery as
we increase in age—and if there are any happy
they are those of thoughtless childhood.

I THEN viewed the world at a distance in
perspective. I thought mankind appeared happy
in the midst of pleasures that flowed round
them. I now find it a deception, and am tempted
sometimes to wish myself a child again. Happy
are the dreams of infancy, and happy their
harmless pursuits! I saw the *ignis fatuus,* and
have been running after it, but now I return
from the search. I return and bring back disappointment. As I reflect on these scenes of
infantine ignorance, I feel my heart interested,
and become sensibly affected—and however
futile these feelings may appear as I communicate them to you—they are feelings I venture

to assert which every one must have experienced who is possessed of a heart of sensibility.

Adieu!

LETTER XLVII.

HARRINGTON *to* WORTHY.

BOSTON.

I NO longer receive satisfaction from the enjoyments of the world—society is distasteful to me—my favourite authors I have entirely relinquished—In vain I try to forget myself, or seek for consolation—my repose is interrupted by distressing visions of the night —my thoughts are broken—I cannot even think regularly.

HARRIOT is very weak—there is no hope of her life.

Adieu!

[141]

LETTER XLVIII.

HARRINGTON *to* WORTHY.

BOSTON.

MY dear friend, I have a great desire to see you—I wish you could come home speedily—I must be short—I have some serious business to do.

Farewel!

P.S. THEY say life is a blessing and it is our duty to improve and enjoy it; but when life becomes insupportable and we find no blessing in it—have we not a right to resign it?

Farewel!

LETTER XLIX.

The Hon. Mr. HARRINGTON
to the Rev. Mr. HOLMES.

BOSTON.

ACCUMULATED sorrows continue
to break over my devoted head. *Harriot* is at
times deprived of her reason, and we have no
expectation of her recovery—my son is deeply
affected—he seems strangely disordered.

REVOLVING in my mind all these things, and
the unhappy affair that led to them, the whole
train of my past life returned fresh upon my
mind. Pained with the disagreeable picture, and
oppressed with the weight of my affliction, I
sunk down to sleep: These circumstances had
so strongly impressed my imagination that they
produced the following Dream—My blood is
chilled with horrour as I write.

METHOUGHT I suddenly found myself in a
large, open field, waste and uncultivated—here
I wandered in a solitary manner for some time
—grief seized my heart at the awful appear-

ance of the place, and I cried aloud—"How long shall I travel here, alone and friendless— a dusky mist swims before my sight, and the obscure horizon seems only to inclose this dismal wild!" Having advanced a few steps, I thought a light at a distance appeared to my doubtful view. Faint with fatigue, I approached it, and had the satisfaction to behold a person of the most benign aspect—a quiet serenity was painted on his brow, and happiness ineffable beamed from his divine countenance—Joy leaped in my bosom, and in the ecstacy of passion I endeavoured to clasp the blessed spirit to my heart; but it vanished in my embrace.

"TEACH me, blessed shade," said I, with a trembling voice—"teach me to find the habitations of men—What do I here?—Why am I doomed to explore the barren bosom of this baleful desert?" "*This,*" returned the spirit, in a voice, which, while it commanded veneration and love, struck awe and terrour into my soul —"*This* is not the habitation of the sons of mortality—it is the place appointed to receive the souls of all men, after they have resigned the bodies they animated on earth. Those who have violated the laws of reason, humanity, religion, and have dishonoured their God, here meet the punishment due to their crimes.

"ATTEND me, therefore, and view the condition of those thoughtless souls, who, a few

[144]

days ago, were upon earth immersed in pleasure, luxury and vice—Regardless of futurity,
and unprepared for their eternal summons to
another world—and who persisted in the delight of their own eyes in opposition to the
divine law, and deaf to the voice of reclaiming
virtue. These, the sons of folly and riot, are
smitten by the angel of death, while they are
yet drinking of the bowl of vice—while the
words of blasphemy yet dwell upon their
tongues. And when their unhappy spirits sink
to these infernal regions, their surviving companions rehearse their funeral panegyricks—
the praise of one is, that he could drink the
longest—the merit of another, that he could
sing a good song—a third secures his fame
by being excellent in mimickry and buffoonery
—How unhappy must he be, who leaves no
other testimony of his usefulness behind him!

"how different is the fate of the good man:
While upon earth his life is employed in the
cause of virtue—The happiness he bestows on
those around him is reflected back with tenfold
reward; and when he takes rank in that happy
place, where there is fulness of joy, and leaves
the world of mankind, what numbers are joined
in the general concern for his loss—The aged,
while they prepare for the same journey, delight to dwell on his good actions—the virgin
strews flowers on his grave, and the poet con-

sumes the midnight oil to celebrate his virtues."

THERE was so much benignity in every word and action of my attendant, that I found myself imperceptibly attached to him. My attention to his discourse had prevented me from observing the progress we had made—for we had arrived at a place encircled with high walls —a great gate, at the command of my guide, instantly flew open—"Follow me," said he—I tremblingly obeyed.——

MY ears were instantaneously filled with the faint cries of those here doomed to receive the rewards of their demerits. Looking earnestly forward, I beheld a group of unhappy wretches —I observed a person who was continually tormenting them—he held in one hand a whip, the lashes of which were composed of adders, and the stings of scorpions; and in the other a large mirrour, which, when he held up to the faces of the tormented, exhibited their crimes in the most flagrant colours, and forced them to acknowledge the justness of their punishment. "These," said my guide, "who are scourged with a whip of scorpions, and who start with horrour at the reflection of their deeds upon earth, are the souls of the Gambler —the Prodigal—the Duelist, and the Ingrate.

"THOSE whom you see yonder," continued he, "those wasted, emaciated spirits, are the souls of the Envious—they are doomed to view the most beautiful fruit, which they can never taste, and behold pleasures which they can never enjoy. This punishment is adjudged them because most of those vile passions, by which men suffer themselves to be ruled, bring real evil, for promised good.

"FOR this reason the allwise Judge hath ordered the same passions still to inflame those ghosts, with which they were possessed on earth—Observe yon despicable crew!—behold the sin of Avarice!—those sordid ghosts are the souls of Misers—Lo! they eye their delightful bags with horrid pleasure; and with a ghastly smile, brood over their imaginary riches. Unable to carry their wealth about with them, they are confined to one spot, and in one position. This infernal joy is the source of their tortures, for behold them start at every sound, and tremble at the flitting of a shade. Thus are they doomed to be their own tormentors—to pore over their gold with immortal fear, apprehension, and jealousy, and to guard their ideal wealth with the tears of care, and the eyes of eternal watchfulness.

"BEHOLD here," continued my guide, "the miserable division of Suicides!"—"Unhappy they!" added I, "who, repining at the ills of life, raised the sacrilegious steel against their own bosoms! How vain the reiterated wish to again animate the breathless clay—to breathe the vital air—and to behold the cheering luminary of Heaven!"—"Upbraid me not—O my father!" cried a voice—I looked up, and thought my son appeared among them—but immediately turning from so shocking a spectacle, I suddenly beheld my once loved *Maria*—"O delight of my youth! do I behold thee once more!—Let me hide my sorrows in thy friendly bosom." I advanced towards her—but she flew from me with scorn and indignation—"O speak! *Maria!* speak to me!" She pointed with her finger to a group of spirits, and was out of sight in a moment.

"LET me," said my conductor, "prepare you for a more dreadful sight." The increasing melancholy, and affecting gloom of the situation, forboded something terrifying to my soul —I looked toward the place where *Maria* had pointed, and saw a number of souls remote from any division of the unhappy. In their countenances were depicted more anguish, sorrow and despair—I turned my head immediately from this dreadful sight, without distinguishing the nature of their torments. Quivering with horrour, I inquired who they were —"These," answered my guide, with a sigh, "are the miserable race of SEDUCERS.—Repentance and shame drive them far from the rest of the accursed. Even the damned look on them with horrour, and thank fate their crimes are not of so deep a die."

HE had hardly finished, when a demon took hold of me, and furiously hurried me in the midst of this unhappy group—I was so terrified that it immediately roused me from my sleep.——

EVEN now, while I write to you, my good friend, my hand trembles with fear at the painful remembrance—Yet

——'Twas but a dream, but then
So terrible, it shakes my very soul.——

Farewel!

LETTER L.

HARRIOT *to* HARRINGTON.

BOSTON.

MUST I then forget the endearments of the lover, and call you by the name of brother? But does our friendship remain upon this foundation? Is this all that unites us? And has there subsisted nothing more tender—a sentiment more voluntary in our hearts? My feelings affirm that there has. At the hour of our first interview I felt the passion kindle in my breast: Insensible of my own weakness, I indulged its increasing violence and delighted in the flame that fired my reason and my senses. Do you remember our walks, our conversations, our diversions?—The remembrance of these things fill my mind with inconceivable torture—they seem to reproach me with unmerited criminality—I deprecate, I detest all these scenes of gaity and frivolity—yet I have preserved my innocence and my virtue—what then have I to deprecate, what have I to detest?

ALAS! how have we been forming schemes of happiness, and mocking our hearts with unsubstantial joys. Farewel! farewel! ye gilded scenes of imagination. How have we been deluded by visionary prospects, and idly dwelt upon that happiness which was never to arrive. How fleeting have been the days that were thus employed!—when anticipation threw open the gates of happiness, and we vainly contemplated the approach of bliss;—when we beheld in reversion, the pleasures of life, and fondly promised ourselves, one day to participate in them;—when we beheld in the magick mirrour of futurity, the lively group of loves that sport in the train of joy. We observed in transports of delight the dear delusion, and saw them, as it were, in bodily form pass in review before us; as the fabled hero views the region of præ-existant spirits, and beholds a race of men yet to be born.

SUCH was our hope, but even this fairy antic-ipation was not irrational. We were happy in idea, nor was the reality far behind. And why is the vision vanished? O! I sink, I die, when I reflect—when I find in my *Harrington* a brother—I am penetrated with inexpressible grief—I experience uncommon sensations—I start with horrour at the idea of incest—of ruin—of perdition.

HOW do I lament this fatal discovery, that includes the termination of a faithful love! I think of him to whom I have resolved to be eternally constant—and ah! how often have I resolved it in my heart. I indulge, in idea, the recollection of his caresses—of his protesta-tions, and of his truth and sincerity—I be-come lost in a wilderness, and still I travel on, and find myself no nearer an escape. I cherish the dear idea of a lover—I see the danger and do not wish to shun it, because, to avoid it, is to forget it—And can I, at one stroke, erase from my mind the remembrance of all in which my heart used to delight? Ah! I have not the

fortitude—I have not the virtue, to "forget myself to marble." On the contrary, I strive no
longer to remember our present connexion. I
endeavour to forget—I curse the idea of a
brother—my hand refuses to trace the word,
and yet

————The name appears
Already written; blot it out my tears!

AH, whence this sorrow that invests my soul!
This gloom that darkens—this fire of impas-
sioned grief, that involves all my thoughts!
why do I rave, and why do I again abandon
myself to despair! Come, O *Harrington!* be
a friend, a protector, a brother—be him, on
whom I could never yet call by the tender, the
endearing title of *parent*. I will reverence him
in whom all the charities of life are united—I
will be dutiful and affectionate to you, and you
shall be unto me as a father—I will bend on
the knee of respect and love, and will receive
your blessing.

WHY did you go away so soon? Why leave
me when I was incapable of bidding you adieu?
When you pressed my cheek with the kiss of
love, of fraternal affection, what meant its conscious glow? What meant the ebullition of my
veins, the disorder of my nerves, the intoxica-

tion of my brain, the blood that mantled in my heart? My hand trembled, and every object seemed to swim before my doubtful view— Amidst the struggle of passion, how could I pronounce the word—how could I call you by the title of brother. True—I attempted to articulate the sound, but it died upon my tongue, and I sank motionless into your arms.

——ALLIED by birth, and in mind, and similar in age—and in thought still more intimately connected, the sympathy which bound our souls together, at first sight, is less extraordinary. Shall we any longer wonder at its irresistible impulse?—Shall we strive to oppose the *link of nature* that draws us to each other? When I reflect on this, I relapse into weakness and tenderness, and become a prey to warring passions. I view you in two distinct characters: If I indulge the idea of one, the other becomes annihilated, and I vainly imagine I have my choice of a brother or——

I AM for a while calm—but alas! how momentary is that calmness; I dwell with rapture on what fancy has represented; but is the choice regulated by virtue? Is it prompted by reason? I recollect myself, and endeavour to rouse my prudence and fortitude; I abhor my conduct, and wish for obscurity and forgetfulness. Who can bear the torment of fluctuating passion?

How deplorable is the contest? The head and the heart are at variance, but when Nature pleads, how feeble is the voice of Reason? Yet, when Reason is heard in her turn, how criminal appears every wish of my heart? What remorse do I experience? What horrours surround me? Will my feeble frame, already wasted by a lingering decline, support these evils? Will the shattered, frail bark outride the tempest, and will the waves of affliction beat in vain? Virtue, whose precepts I have not forgotten, will assist me—if not to *surmount,* at least to *suffer* with fortitude and patience.

oh! I fear, I fear my decaying health—If I must depart, let me beseech you to forget me— I know the strength of your passion, and I dread the fatal consequences my departure may occasion you.

once more let me intreat you, my dear friend, to arm yourself with every virtue which is capable of sustaining the heaviest calamity. Let the impetuosity of the lover's passion be forgotten in the undisturbed quietness of the brother's affection, and may all the blessings that life can supply be yours—Seek for content, and you will find it, even though we should never meet again in this world.

Adieu!

LETTER LI.

MYRA *to* Mrs. HOLMES.

BOSTON.

THE curtain is dropped, and the scene of life is forever closed—THE LOVELY HARRIOT IS NO MORE.

SHE is fit to appear in Heaven, for her life was a scene of purity and innocence—If there is any consolation to be felt by a survivor, it is in the reflection of the amiable qualities of the deceased. My heart shall not cease to cherish her idea, for she was beautiful without artifice, and virtuous without affectation.

See! there all pale and dead she lies;
Forever flow my streaming eyes——
There dwelt the fairest—lovliest mind,
Faith, sweetness, wit together join'd.
　　Dwelt faith and wit and sweetness there?
O! view the change, and drop a tear.

MY brother is exceedingly agitated—He will never support this disastrous stroke—Nothing can attract his attention—nothing allay his grief—but it is the affliction of reason and not of weakness——God grant that it prove not fatal to him.

Adieu!—Adieu!—

LETTER LII.

HARRINGTON *to* WORTHY.

BOSTON.

SHE is gone—she is dead—she who was the most charming, the most gentle, is gone—You may come—you may desire to behold all that was lovely—but your eyes will not see her.

YES! I raved—I was distracted—but now I am calm and dispassionate—I am smooth as the surface of a lake—I shall see her again.

WHEN our spirits are disencumbered of this load of mortality, and they wing their flight to the celestial regions, shall we not then know those who were dear to us in this world? Shall we not delight in their society, as we have done in this state of existence? Yes—certainly

[156]

we shall—we shall find them out in Heaven—
there alone is happiness—there shall I meet her
—there our love will not be a crime—Let me
indulge this thought—it gives a momentary
joy to my heart—it removes the dark mist that
swims before my eyes—it restores tranquillity;
but the more I reflect on this thought—the
more I long to be there—the more I detest this
world and all it contains. I sigh to fly away
from it.

LETTER LIII.

HARRINGTON *to* WORTHY.

BOSTON.

INGRATITUDE is a predominant
principle in the conduct of man. The perfidious
———, who owes to me his reputation and
fortune, and with whom I intrusted a great
part of my property, has deceived me. This
affair will materially retard my business.

TO be unfortunate in trade is not worth a
sigh—to receive inattention and incivility does
not merit a frown; but *Ingratitude*—it is this
that cuts to the quick. Yet I freely give him

my pity; for what man, who considered for a moment the inconsistency of the human heart, would hurl the thunderbolt of indignation at the head of an ingrate? What an important little thing is man! he contrives to overreach his neighbour, and mount to the enjoyment of riches, ambition and splendour; but remembers not the period of enjoyment—that his life is a day, and his space a point!

NATURALISTS inform us of insects whose term of existence is confined to a few hours— What is the business and importance of such a life?

WOULD not a being, whose *circle of living* is immensity of ages, inquire with equal propriety, "What is the importance of *man*—What actions can he perform—What happiness can he enjoy, whose insignificant life is circumscribed to seventy years?"——In this point of view I behold the tinsel, the vanity and noise of the world, and the little plots and cunning artifices of mankind to cheat and ruin one another.

INGRATITUDE, then, is constitutional, and inseparable from human nature, but it ought not to fill us with surprize, because it is no new discovery—It has ever been invariably the characteristick of man. Is not the page of antiquity distained with the blood of those who ought to have received honour and adoration? Behold

the brilliant race of the world's benefactors:
Consider their benevolent actions, and regard
their ungrateful return—these benefactors,
who have been sent from heaven to inform and
entertain mankind, to defend the world from
the arm of tyranny, and to open the gates of
salvation, have been despised, and banished,
and poisoned and crucified.

BEHOLD the support of the *Roman* power, the
invincible *Belisarius!* who protected his country
from the ravage of the *Huns,* and displayed
the *Roman* eagle in every quarter of the globe!
Behold him fall a sacrifice to malice, to faction
and ingratitude! Behold him cast out by the
country he had defended, and for which he had
wasted his life to protect and honour, and left
alone to deplore his unfortunate condition, when
he was old, and blind, and naked and miserable!

UNFORTUNATE is the man who trusts his happiness to the precarious friendship of the world
—I every day become more of a misanthrope,
and see nothing to increase my desire of living,
but your esteem and affection. I want advice,
but am too proud to let the world know I am
weak enough to be under obligation to any one
else.

THAT you may never want friends or advice,
is the sincere prayer of

Your &c.

LETTER LIV.

HARRINGTON *to* WORTHY.

BOSTON.

ALL the scenes of my past life return fresh upon my memory. I examine every circumstance as they pass in review before me—I see nothing to cause any disagreeable or unwelcome sensations—no terrour upbraids me—no reproaching conscience stings my bosom as I reflect on the actions that are past. With her I expected happiness—I have expected a vain thing—for there is none—She is gone—gone to a far country—she is preparing a place for me—a place of unutterable bliss—But ah! an immeasurable gulph lies between us—Who can tell the distance that separates us? What labour —what toil—what pain must be endured in traversing the thorny paths that lead to her blessed abode?—And will she not receive me into those happy regions with as much joy— with as sincere a welcome—if I cut short my journey?—And will not the Eternal Dispenser of Good, pardon the awful deed that frees me from this world of misery—the deed by which I obtrude myself into his divine presence?

WHY must I wait the lingering hand of the grisly messenger to summon me to the world above?

LETTER LV.

HARRINGTON *to* WORTHY.

BOSTON.

AM I a child that I should weep?— I have been meditating on the cause of my calamities—Why did my father love *Maria*— or rather, why did I love their *Harriot?* Curse on this tyrant custom that dooms such helpless children to oblivion or infamy! Had I known her to have been my sister, my love would have been regular—I should have loved her as a sister—I should have marked her beauty—I should have delighted in protecting it. I should have observed her growing virtues—I should have been happy in cherishing their growth. But alas! She is gone——and I cannot stay—I stand on the threshold of a vast eternity.

LETTER LVI.

HARRINGTON *to* WORTHY.

BOSTON.

I AM determined to quit this life. I feel much easier since my determination. The step must not be taken with rashness. I must be steady—calm—collected—I will endeavour to be so.——

HER eager solicitation—the anxiety she always expressed for me————When I think she is no more, it wrings my heart with grief, and fills my eyes with tears——

——I MUST go——

THE idea chills me—I am frozen with horrour—cold damps hang on my trembling body —My soul is filled with a thousand troubled sensations——I must depart—it must be so— My love for thee, O *Harriot!* is dearer than life—Thou hast first sat out—and I am to follow.——

WERE it possible that I *could live* with her, should I be happy? Would her presence restore peace and tranquillity to my disordered mind?

Ah no! it never would *here*—it *never* would. I will fly to the place where she is gone—our love will there be refined—it will be freed from all criminality—I will lay my sorrows before her—and she shall wipe away all tears from my eyes.

WHEN the disembodied spirit flies above—when it leaves behind the senseless clay, and wings its flight—it matters not with me what they do with his remains.

> Cover his head with a clod or a stone,
> It is all one—it is all one!——

LETTER LVII.

HARRINGTON *to* WORTHY.

BOSTON.

THE longer I live, and the more I see of the misery of life—the more my desire of living is extinguished. What I formerly esteemed trifles, and would not deign to term misfortunes, now appear with a formidable aspect—though I once thought them harmless,

and innoxious to my peace, they assume new
terrours every day.—But is not this observation general? It is—It is thus every son of
human nature, gradually wishes for death, and
neglects to seek for, and improve those com-
forts, which by diligent search there is a possibility of attaining.

AM I to reason from analogy? I know what
has been—the afflictions I have felt; but what
is the prospect before me? The path is darkened
by mists—

Puzzled in mazes, and perplex'd with errours—

Who is there hardy enough to try its difficulties? Is not the view horrible! My pains and
anxieties have been severe—those, which, if I
live, I shall suffer, may be yet more so—This
idea sinks me to despair.

AS a thing becomes irksome to us, our detestation is always encreased—Whatever object
is disagreeable, we pine and sicken until it is
moved out of sight. Life growing upon one in
this manner—increasing in horrour—with continual apprehension of death—a certainty of
surviving every enjoyment, and no prospect of
being delivered from suspense—it is intolerable—he will assuredly be tempted to terminate
the business with his own hand.

LETTER LVIII.

WORTHY *to* HARRINGTON.

BELLEVIEW.

You argue as if your reason were perverted—Let your mind be employed, and time will wear out these gloomy ideas; for it is certainly a truth, that *the love of life increases with age*—Your letters, therefore, are predicated on the most erroneous principles.

REMEMBER the story of the old man, who had been buried in a dungeon the greater part of his life, and who was liberated at an advanced age. He viewed, once more, the light of the sun, and the habitations of men—he had come into a new order of beings, but found their manners distasteful—In the midst of the sunshine of the world, he remembered the prison, where he had wasted his life, and he sighed to be again immured within its walls.

SUCH is our passion for life; we love it because we know it; and our attachment becomes the more riveted, the longer we are acquainted with it—Our prison grows familiar—we contemplate its horrours—but however gloomy the walls that surround us, there is not one but sets a full value on his dreary existence—there is not one but finds his partiality for his dungeon increase, in proportion to the time he hath occupied it—for among the race of human beings confined to this narrow spot—how few are they who are hardy enough to break their prison?

LET us watch over all we do with an eye of scrutiny—the world will not examine the causes that give birth to our actions—they do not weigh the motives of them—they do not consider those things which influence our conduct —but as that conduct is more or less advantageous to society, they deem it madness or wisdom, or folly or prudence—Remember this——

Adieu!

LETTER LIX.

HARRINGTON *to* WORTHY.

BOSTON.

Y OU are egregiously mistaken, argue as you will.—My perceptions are as clear as any one's—The burden that is at first heavy and inconvenient, galls us as we proceed—it soon becomes intolerable, we sink under its weight, and lie gasping in the publick way long before night.

AS to the world—who strives to please it, will be deservedly rewarded—he will reap his labour for his pains—Let it judge of my conduct. I despise its opinion—*Independency of spirit* is my motto—I think for myself.

LETTER LX.

HARRINGTON *to* WORTHY.

BOSTON.

H OW vain is the wish that sighs for the enjoyment of worldly happiness. Our imagination dresses up a phantom to impose on our reason: As *Pygmalion* loved the work of his own hand—so do we fall in love with the offspring of our brain. But our work illudes our embrace—we find no substance in it—and then fall a weeping and complain of disappointment. Miserable reasoners are we all.

WHY should I mourn the loss of *Harriot* any

[167]

longer? Such is my situation—in the midst of anxiety and distress, I complain of what cannot be remedied.—I lament the loss of that which is irretrievable: So on the sea-beat shore, the hopeless maid, unmindful of the storm, bewails her drowned lover.

LETTER LXI.

WORTHY *to* HARRINGTON.

BELLEVIEW.

I THANK you for your letters, but I wish you had something better for the subject of them—the sad repetition of your feelings and sorrows, pains me exceedingly—I promise to be with you soon—perhaps before you can receive this letter.

WHATEVER concerns my friend, most sensibly affects me—You, *Harrington,* are the friend of my heart, and nothing has so much grieved me as the story of your misfortunes.

IT is a maxim well received, and seems to be admitted an article in the moral creed of mankind, "that the enjoyments of life do not com-

pensate the miseries." Since, then, we are born
to suffer, and pain must attend us in all the
stages of our journey, let us philosophically
welcome our companion. The most eligible plan
we can adopt, is to be contented in the condition
that Providence hath assigned us. Let us trust
that our burden will not be heavier than we
can bear—When we adopt this plan, and are
sensible we have this trust, our lesson is complete—we have learned all—we are arrived to
the perfection of sublunary happiness.

DO not think I am preaching to you a mere
sermon of morality—let me impress your mind
with the folly of repining, and the blessing of a
contented mind.

LET me intreat you not to puzzle your brain
with vain speculations—if you are disposed to
argue, do not put foolish cases that never
existed—take the light of facts, and reason
from them.

WHEN we are surrounded with the miseries
of life—the baseness of false friends—the
malice of enemies—when we are inveloped in
those anxious fears, the result of too much
sensibility, human nature feels a degree of op-
pression, which, without a manly exertion of
reason and this practical philosophy, would be
intolerable. I have heard you mention *St. Evremond,* as a philosopher of this kind. Arm your-

self with his prudence and fortitude—he, though in exile—though reduced almost to penury, and labouring under the disadvantages of a bad constitution, lived to be a very old man; he established a course of rational pleasures—for when the mind is employed, we regret the loss of time—we become avaricious of life.

WHEN misfortunes come upon us without these consolations, it is hard, I acknowledge, to buffet the storm—it is then human frailty is most apparent—there is nothing left to hope —Reason is taken from the helm of life—and Nature—helpless, debilitated Nature—lost to herself, and every social duty, splits upon the rocks of despair and suicide. We have seen several examples of this—By exploring, and therefore shunning the causes, let us avoid the catastrophe.

THE pensive and melancholy will muse over the ordinary accidents of life, and swell them, by the power of imagination, to the heaviest calamities. Hence we find a treacherous friend will sensibly affect some men, and a capricious mistress will destroy a real lover: Hence people in misfortune frequently construe the slightest inattention into neglect and insult, and deem their best friends false and ungrateful. The sting of ingratitude deeply pierces the heart of sensibility.

THE passions and affections which govern mankind are very inconsistent. Men, confined to the humble walks of life, sigh for the enjoyment of wealth and power, which, when obtained, become loathsome—The mind unaccustomed to such an easy situation, is discontented, and longs to be employed in those things in which it was formerly exercised.

THE greatest rulers and potentates become unhappy—they wish for the charms of solitude and retirement, which, when attained, become more irksome than their former condition—*Charles* the Fifth, of *Spain,* resolved to taste the pleasures of a recluse life, by abdicating the throne—he soon found his imagination had deceived him, and repented of the step he had taken. This lazy life, when compared to the business and grandeur of a court, became tasteless and insipid.—"The day," says a historian, "he resigned his crown to his son, was the very day in which he repented making him such a present."

IT is a great art to learn to be happy in the state in which we are placed—I advise you to mingle in the concerns of your acquaintances— be cheerful and undisturbed, nor give yourself up to those gloomy ideas, which tend only to make you more wretched—If such obtrude themselves, avoid being alone—I had rather be a dupe to my imagination than sacrifice an hour's easiness to my sensibility or understanding. Determine to be happy, and you will be so——

God be with you!

———

LETTER LXII.

HARRINGTON *to* WORTHY.

BOSTON.

WHEN we seek for diversion in any place, and there is nothing to be found that we wish, it is certainly time to depart.

TOMORROW I go—There is nothing here that can calm the tumult of my soul—I fly from the sight of the human countenance—I fly from the face of day—I fly from books—Books that could always cheer me in a melancholy moment, are now terrifying—They recal scenes to my recollection that are past—pleasant scenes that I am never more to enjoy. They present pictures of futurity—of gloomy futurity—I just opened a book, and these are the words that I read:—"The time of my fading is near, and the blast that shall scatter my leaves. Tomorrow shall the traveller come, he that saw me in my beauty shall come; his eyes will search the field, but they will not find me."

THESE words pierce me to the quick—they are a dismal prospect of my approaching fate.

TOMORROW I shall go—But ah! whither?——

O! MY friend, when we find nothing we desire in this world, it is time to depart. To live is a disgrace—to die is a duty.

Farewel!

LETTER LXIII.

WORTHY *to Mrs.* HOLMES.

BOSTON.

I ARRIVED in town last evening—you desired me to write you a statement of affairs as I should find them here—and of my marriage with the amiable *Myra*—I promised to obey—but how little do we know of the termination or consequence of the most probable event!

I SAW my beloved—her eyes were yet heavy and smarting with weeping for the death of *Harriot*—and *this,* once the house of joy and cheerfulness, is turned into the house of mourning. My unfortunate friend had just then fallen into a calm sleep, and it was impossible to see him—it was what I very much desired—but it was the wish of the family that I should desist for the present—he had not slept the evening before—he had been heard walking across his chamber all the night, with little intermission, oftentimes talking to himself in a passionate tone of voice.

THIS melancholy account deeply affected me —and I parted from my beloved, praying Heaven to give her consolation, and to be the support of my disordered friend.

IT is with difficulty I bring myself to the serious and painful employment of being the informer of unwelcome tidings—my heart feels the wound—vainly it tells me my friend is no more—my hand reluctantly traces—my friend —my *Harrington* is no more.

EARLY this morning I was surprised with a visit from a gentleman, whom I had formerly seen at *Myra's*—it was the same neighbour who informed *Harrington* of his affinity to

Harriot—he found a difficulty in his utterance
—he told me, with trembling lips, my young
friend *Harrington* was dead—"He has killed
himself," said I—he asked me if I had heard
the news—I told him my heart presaged it.

WHEN any uncommon event happens to us,
we often have a presentiment of it—The circumstances of his death are these:—At midnight the gentleman heard the report of the
pistol, and went into the house—he found the
unhappy youth weltering in his blood—few
signs of life remained—the ball had entered
his brain—the surgeon came, but in a few hours
he was cold. A few friends were requested to
attend—and this gentleman had called upon me,
by desire of *Myra*.

IT is not possible to describe the distress of
the family and connexions—I shall leave it to
your imagination.

A LETTER that he had written for me, laid
unsealed upon the table, and *The Sorrows of
Werter* was found lying by its side. I send you
the letter—it appears to have been written at
intervals, and expresses the disorder and agitation of his mind.

Adieu!

LETTER LXIV.

HARRINGTON *to* WORTHY.

*H*ARRIOT is dead—and the world to me is a dreary desert—I prepare to leave it —the fatal pistol is charged—it lies on the table by me, ready to perform its duty—but that duty is delayed till I take my last farewel of the best of friends.

YOUR letter is written with the impetuosity of an honest heart; it expresses great sincerity and tenderness.

I THANK you for all your good advice—it comes too late——O *Worthy!* she is dead—she is gone—never to return, never again to cheer my heart with her smiles and her amiable manners—her image is always before me—and can I forget her?—No!—She is continually haunting my mind, impressing the imagination with ideas of excellence—but she is dead—all that delighted me is become torpid—is descended into the cold grave.

[176]

- - - - With thee
Certain my resolution is to die;
How can I live without thee—how forego
Thy converse sweet, and love so dearly join'd,
To live again in these wild woods forlorn?
- - - - - - - - - -
- - - - loss of thee
Will never from my heart—no! no!—I feel
The link of nature draw me.
- - - - From thy state
Mine never shall be parted, bliss or woe.

THOU hast sat out on a long journey—but you shall not go alone—I hasten to overtake thee. My resolution is not to be diverted—is not to be shaken—I will not be afraid—I am inexorable——

——I HAVE just seen my father—he is dejected—sullen grief is fixed on his brow— he tells me I am very ill—I looked at *Myra*— she wiped her face with her handkerchief— perhaps they did not imagine this was the last time they were to behold me.

SHE mentioned the name of *Worthy,* but my thoughts were differently engaged. She repeated your name, but I took no heed of it.—— Take her, my *Worthy—Myra* is a good girl—

[177]

take her—comfort her. Let not my departure interrupt your happiness—perhaps it may for a short time. When the grass is grown over my grave, lead her to it, in your pensive walks—point to the spot where my ashes are deposited—drop one tear on the remembrance of a friend, of a brother—but I cannot allow you to be grieved—grieve for me! Wretch that I am—why do I delay——

——I WISH I could be buried by the side of her, then should the passenger who knows the history of our unfortunate loves, say— "Here lies *Harrington* and his *Harriot*—in their lives they loved, but were unhappy—in death they sleep undivided."—Guardian spirits will protect the tomb which conceals her body —the body where every virtue delighted to inhabit.——

DO not judge too rashly of my conduct—let me pray you to be candid—I have taken advantage of a quiet moment, and written an Epitaph—If my body were laid by hers, the inscription would be pertinent. Let no one concerned be offended at the moral I have chosen to draw from our unfortunate story.

——MY heart sinks within me—the instrument of death is before me—farewell! farewel!—My soul sighs to be freed from its con-

finement—Eternal Father! accept my spirit
——Let the tears of sorrow blot out my guilt
from the book of thy wrath.

LETTER LXV.

WORTHY *to* Mrs. HOLMES.

BOSTON.

WE have surmounted the perform-
ance of the last scene of our tragedy, with less
difficulty and distress than I imagined. Great
numbers crouded to see the body of poor *Harrington;* they were impressed with various emotions, for their sympathizing sorrow could not
be concealed—Indeed a man without sensibility
exhibits no sign of a soul. I was struck with
admiration at the observations of the populace,
and the justness of the character they drew of
the deceased. "Alas!" said one—"poor youth,
thou art gone. Thou wast of a promising
genius, of violent passions, thou wast possessed
of a too nice sensibility, and a dread of shame.
It is only such an one who would take the
trouble to kill himself. Ah! poor well natured,

warm hearted, hot headed youth—how my heart bleeds for you! We consider thee as the dupe of Nature, and the sacrifice of Seduction." —The old father hears this, and becomes overwhelmed with shame and sorrow.

THE jury which sat upon the body of our friend, after mature consideration, brought in their verdict SUICIDE. The rigour of the law was not executed—the body was privately taken away, and I saw it deposited by the side of his faithful *Harriot.*

I SEND you inclosed a copy of the Monumental Inscription, as written by *Harrington.* I found it with many loose papers. It contains the story of our unfortunate friends, and a profitable moral is deduced from it.

THOUGH a few weeks begin to spread a calm over our passions, yet the recollection of our misfortunes will sometimes cause a momentary agitation, as the ocean retains its swell, after the storm subsides.

Adieu!

Monumental Inscription.

THOU who shalt wander o'er these humble plains,
Where one kind grave their hapless dust contains,

[180]

O pass not on—if merit claim a tear,
Or dying virtue cause a sigh sincere.
Here rest their heads, consign'd to parent earth,
Who to one common father ow'd their birth;
Unknown this union—Nature still presides,
And Sympathy unites, whom Fate divides.
They see—they love—but heav'n their passion
   tries,
Their *love* sustains it, but their *mortal* dies.
Stranger! contemplate well before you part,
And take this serious counsel to thy heart:
Does some fair female of unspotted fame,
Salute thee, smiling, with a father's name,
Bid her detest the fell Seducer's wiles,
Who smiles to win—and murders as he smiles.
If ever wandering near this dark recess,
Where guardian spirits round the ether press;
Where, on their urn, celestial care descends,
Two lovers come, whom fair success attends,
"O'er the pale marble shall they join their heads,
"And drink the falling tears each other sheds,
"Then sadly say, with mutual pity mov'd,
"*O! may we never love as these have lov'd.*"

The END.

APPENDIXES

TEXTUAL INTRODUCTION

THE *Power of Sympathy* was first published in Boston by Isaiah Thomas and Company toward the end of January, 1789. An advertisement in the *Independent Chronicle* for 22 January referred to the novel as "this day published," but the same notice also appeared in the *Massachusetts Spy* for 29 January and the Boston *Gazette* for 2 February. Copies were offered bound in leather at nine shillings or stitched in blue paper at six shillings, eight pence. This first edition is in two volumes, in gatherings of six leaves. Copies also occur in contemporary bindings as two volumes bound in one. The volumes collate: [Vol. I] A–I⁶ K–L⁶ M⁴ [Vol. II] π² N–U⁶ W–Z⁶ &⁶; [Vol. I] pp. *i–v* vi *7* 8–138 *139–40* [Vol. II] *1–3* 4–158 *159–60*. Volume I contains the title page, p. i; verso, p. ii, blank. Dedication, p. iii; verso, p. iv, blank. Preface, pp. v and vi. The text of Letters I–XXVIII occupies pp. 7–138; pp. 139–40 are blank. In Volume II the title page is p. 1; verso, p. 2, blank. The text of Letters XXIX–LXV occupies pp. 3–158; pp. 159–60 are blank.

An engraved frontispiece by Samuel Hill, depicting the scene described in Letter XXI and captioned "O Fatal! Fatal Poison!" is inserted facing the title page of Volume I. This frontispiece occurs in two states, distinguished most easily by the presence or absence of the artist's signature in the lower right-hand corner. Although the *Bibliography of American Literature* (I, 310: Entry 1518) seems to doubt the existence of copies with the unsigned frontispiece, Jacob Blanck has since written (in a letter to the editor, 16 August 1967) that such copies do exist and that "after some study, and the help of competent authority, it was decided that the unsigned plate was a second state." Copies with the unsigned frontispiece are present in the editor's collection, in the Clifton Waller Barrett Collection at the University of Virginia, and in the Lilly Library at Indiana University. Little is known of Samuel Hill, who engraved many portraits and early American views for Thomas's *Massachusetts Magazine*. In *Russell's Gazette* (Boston, 1794), he advertised himself as "engraver and copperplate printer," with a shop at 2 Cornhill.

The only copy in boards, uncut, known to the editor is in the Barrett Collection at Virginia. There can be no question about the fact that this copy is uncut, although the binding may be sophisticated. At the very least, the endpapers appear to be modern insertions. The *Bibliography of American Literature* seems to imply, as does a dealer's description laid in this copy, that this copy (and, presumably, other copies issued in boards) was issued without the frontispiece, but the stub belonging to the missing frontispiece is clearly visible between A6 and B1.

Eleven short passages from the novel appeared on pages 50–53 of the January, 1789, issue of Thomas's *Massachusetts Magazine*. Under the heading, "Beauties of The Power of Sympathy" were included "Beauty" (17.24–18.4; page and line references are to the present edition), "Novels" (28.11–28.19), "Female Study" (31.19–33.8), "Self Knowledge" (40.14–40.24), "Self Complacency" (94.17–94.23), "Sensibility" (104.25–105.17), "Tears" (120.14–120.23), "Ingratitude" (158.24–159.8), "Suicide" (165.7–166.8), "Conscience"

(122.23–123.16), and "Seduction" (116.9–118.6). The variations between the first edition of the novel and the magazine printing of these passages are recorded in a separate table below.

The second edition of *The Power of Sympathy* appeared in 1894 under the imprint: Boston: Printed by Cupples & Patterson and Published by Them at the Back Bay Bookstore, 250 Boylston Street. The editor's introduction, dated June, 19, 1894, is by Walter Littlefield, who signed the 550 numbered copies. This edition attributes the novel to Mrs. Perez Morton (Sarah Wentworth Apthorp). The typography of Littlefield's edition is consciously old-fashioned and imitates the styling of the original, although it cannot be called a type facsimile.

The third printing of the novel appeared in installments in the *Bostonian Magazine*. The October, 1894 (Vol. I, No. 1) issue contains an "Editor's Preface" by A. W. Brayley (pp. 19–23) and the text of Letters I–XI (pp. 24–37). Vol. I, No. 2 (November) contains Letters XII–XXII (pp. 138–49). These first two installments attributed the novel to Mrs. Perez Morton. The December issue (Vol. I, No. 3) contained "The Real Author of 'The Power of Sympathy'" signed by Arthur W. Brayley (pp. 224–33) and Letters XXIII–XXVII (pp. 234–39). The December and subsequent installments attribute the novel to William Hill Brown. Vol. I, No. 4 (January, 1895) contains Letters XXVIII–XXIX (pp. 429–34); Vol. I, No. 5 (February), Letters XXX–XXXVII (pp. 546–51); Vol. I, No. 6 (March), Letters XXXXIII [*sic*, error for XXXVIII] and XXXIX (pp. 615–21); Vol. II, No. 1 (April), Letters XL–XLIX (pp. 39–46); Vol. II, No. 2 (May), Letters L–LX (pp. 172–78); and Vol. II, No. 3 (June), Letters LXI–LXV (pp. 270–74).

In 1937 the Columbia University Press published a

two-volume facsimile of the first edition as Publication No. 38 for The Facsimile Text Society. Volume I contains a valuable six-page "Bibliographical Note" by Milton Ellis. The copy reproduced is that in the New York Public Library. Some retouching was allowed in the production of this facsimile, and its text is consequently unreliable at several points. The only recent printing of the novel is in a text photo-offset from typewriting by New Frontiers Press (Boston, 1961), with a critical introduction by Herbert Brown.

Since no text of the novel after 1789 is based on fresh authority, the first edition of the novel contains the only authoritative text and automatically becomes the copy-text for this edition. There is, of course, a possible second source of authority for those passages printed in the January, 1789, *Massachusetts Magazine*, but the variations between the magazine and book versions of these passages are trivial and almost certainly originated with the compositor(s) who set the magazine text. The documentary form of the first edition has been established through collation of ten copies: a copy in the editor's collection (K); three copies in the Clifton Waller Barrett Collection at the University of Virginia (a copy with a presentation inscription, B1; a copy with the frontispiece in the second, unsigned, state, B2; and an uncut copy, B3); the Mrs. Robert C. Taylor copy at the University of Virginia (T); the New York Public Library copy (N); the Library of Congress copy (L); the Henry E. Huntington Library copy (H); the Newberry Library copy (C); and the Boston Athenaeum copy (A). The first five copies listed have been collated in person; the last five, by means of photographic reproductions. Other copies of the first edition are located at the Columbia University Library, the Lilly Library at Indiana University, the American Antiquarian Society (Isaiah Thomas's own copy), the

Boston Public Library, Harvard University, the John Carter Brown Library at Brown University, the University of Chicago Library, the University of Pennsylvania Library, and the Pennsylvania State University Library; further copies undoubtedly exist.

The collation of the ten copies of the first edition specified above revealed a number of press variants, the majority of which are caused by pulled or loosened type. Although most of these variants are limited to pulled letters and changing spacing, in two instances complete words disappear. One variant involves an erroneous signature which is corrected. All variations noticed in the collations are listed below. The one extremely interesting cluster of press corrections occurs on pp. 99, 100, and 101 of Volume I of the first edition (references in this paragraph are to the original edition). At 99.3, 100.catchword, and 101.1, roman small capitals OPHELIA were altered to italic small capitals. The probable first forme of Sheet I was that containing the inner forme of the outside four leaves of the gathering (1^v, 2, 5^v, 6; pp. 98, 99, 106, 107) and the outer forme of the two-leaf insert (3, 4^v; pp. 101, 104). In four of the ten copies collated, both I2 and I3 are in the uncorrected (roman) state; in five copies, both are in the corrected (italic) state. One copy (B2, Barrett copy with the unsigned frontispiece) contains the uncorrected (roman) state of I2 and the corrected (italic) state of I3. If a rough projection can be made from the ten-copy sample involved in the collations, events occurred as follows: Well into the press run of the first forme of Sheet I, the erroneous use of roman for italic small capitals in the first line of p. 101 (I3) was noticed and altered to italics by stop-press correction. Soon thereafter, the similar error in line 3 of p. 99 (I2) was noticed and corrected. The press run was completed with both readings corrected. The third variant in this cluster is in the

[189]

catchword at the bottom of p. 100 (I2^v), which antici-
pates the reading in the first line of p. 101 (I3). In
this instance, nine copies display the corrected (italic)
reading, and only one copy (B1, Barrett presentation
copy) contains the uncorrected (roman) reading. Again,
if a projection can be made from the small sample, the
erroneous catchword was noticed rather early in the
press run perfecting Sheet I, and the change from
roman to italic was then effected by stop-press correction. The corrected readings are in accord with the
styling of the text, that is, (1) the first word (or where
the first word contains but a single letter, the first two
words) of each normal paragraph is set in small capitals,
and (2) proper names are italicized. Since italic small
capitals were not available in the font employed for the
present text, these readings and the other instances of
italic small capitals in the original have been emended
to roman small capitals. These emendations are recorded in the appropriate table.

Some explanation of the decision to reproduce faith-
fully a number of the features of the styling of the
original edition is in order. The decision to preserve
the feature of setting the opening of each normal paragraph in small capitals is based on interesting evidence
in Letter LXIV. Throughout the novel, after the display
capital and special treatment of the opening of each
letter, all paragraphs begin with one word (or when the
first word is a single letter, two words) in small capitals. But in Letter LXIV, after normal treatment of
the first four paragraphs, full capitals are inserted at the
openings of paragraphs five, seven, and nine, alternated
with regular small capitals at the openings of paragraphs
six and eight. Now, at the end of Letter LXIII, Worthy
had written to Mrs. Holmes: "I send you the letter
[Harrington's last farewell to Worthy]—it appears to
have been written at intervals, and expresses the dis-

order and agitation of his mind." It seems likely that
the unusual use of full capitals which breaks the usual
styling pattern is intended to contribute to the idea that
the letter was "written at intervals" or that the letter
displays the irregularity, "disorder and agitation of his
mind." In view of the fact that this element of styling
can, and probably does, serve to communicate meaning
in this one instance, the decision was made to preserve
this aspect of the original styling. One feature of eighteenth-century styling which has not been preserved is
the repetition of quotation marks at the start of every
line of type in long prose quotations; repeated quotation
marks in poetry, however, have been retained in the
present text. Uses of the long *s* are not reproduced
here.

Conservative editorial principles were applied to other
features of the text. No attempt has been made to bring
uniformity or consistency to the spellings in the text for
two reasons. First, where two variant spellings of a
word exist, there is no external evidence to indicate
which of the spellings is Brown's. Second, there is no
proof that Brown was a consistent speller, and the
variant forms may very well reflect variant forms in
the manuscript which underlies the print. The present
text contains *burden* and *burdened*, but *burthens*,
burthening, and *burthensome* as well. It contains a
mixture of *en-* and *in-* forms of *inquire* and *increase.*
Spellings have been emended only when they are demonstrable errors and not variants acceptable as eighteenth-
century usage according to the *Oxford English Diction-
ary* or various contemporary American texts consulted.
Forms like *gulph, decriped*, and *chymical* are allowed to
stand, but demonstrable errors like *whereeever, up-
bradings*, and *prejuced* (for *prejudiced*) are emended.
An even more conservative position has been maintained
in regard to bringing the grammar of the novel into line

[191]

with present-day standards of correctness. For example, it could be argued that, when the elder Harrington writes, "Perhaps you was always ignorant of the real motives . . .," the grammar may be intended to be a reflection of his depraved morals. No attempt has been made to correct the grammar of Brown's text.

One feature of the original suggests the possibility of distinguishing between the work of the compositors who set the text. Starting on page 25 of Volume II, three hyphens are used, with varying frequency, to represent a one-em dash. Other evidence by which to distinguish compositors is lacking, however, and whether the substitution of the triple hyphens for dashes is caused by a change in compositors or by a shortage for some reason of regular one-em dashes cannot be determined. It is of more than incidental interest to note that the same substitution is found in some of the issues of the *Massachusetts Magazine*, also a product of Thomas's shop. These triple hyphens have been silently emended to one-em dashes in the present text.

The distinction between italic and roman punctuation has caused difficulties. After repeated attempts to distinguish between italic and roman commas, apostrophes, and quotation marks (both single and double) in the original edition, it has been decided that such distinctions are, in fact, impossible to make; indeed, it is probable that the roman and italic sorts of these marks were identical. There can be no argument, however, about the distinction between roman and italic colons, semicolons, exclamation points, and question marks. The following system has been followed: In the present text, italic punctuation has been used in italic contexts; roman, in roman contexts. Commas, apostrophes, and quotation marks have been silently brought into line with this principle. The few demonstrable alterations necessary to bring the appropriate colons and semicolons into line with this principle are recorded as emendations.

The text of the present edition has been prepared in the following manner: A typescript was prepared from, and proofread against, the editor's copy of the first edition and photocopy of the New York Public Library copy (N). This typescript was subsequently collated with the four copies (B1–3, T) at the University of Virginia. Galley proofs were read against the editor's copy of the first edition and against microfilms of the Library of Congress (L) and Boston Athenaeum (A) copies. Page proofs were read against the editor's copy of the original edition and against microfilms of the Henry E. Huntington Library (H) and the Newberry Library (C) copies. All variations whatsoever discovered in the collating and proofreading process were checked against all ten copies, either by consultation with the originals or microfilms thereof. The tables given below present the evidence on which editorial decisions were based and record all variations from the copy-text except for the silent emendations described above.

EMENDATIONS
IN THE COPY-TEXT

EXCEPT for the classes of silent emendations mentioned in the Textual Introduction, all departures from the copy-text are listed here. The page and line references and the readings given first are those of the present text; the subsequent readings are those of the first edition.

29.5	*Worthy;*] *Worthy;*
29.15	'to] "to
29.17	consumption.'] consumption."
31.19	observed,"] observed,_∧_
31.20	"in] _∧_in
33.5	'Lost] "Lost
33.6	'To] "To
33.6	*joy.*'] *joy.*"
36.7	'They] "They
36.8	'In] "In
36.8	mankind.' "] mankind."
40.14	"OUR] _∧_OUR
43.16	inadvertantly——"] inadvertantly——_∧_
56.4	Wherever] Whereever
58.2	*Harriot;*] *Harriot;*
60.3	upbraidings] upbradings

62.15	compunction] compuction
63.3	OPHELIA] italic small caps
64.4	OPHELIA] italic small caps
67.20	Ophelia.] Ophelia_∧
74.22	'With] _∧With
74.26	mine.'] mine._∧
75.22	*betray:*] *betray:*
77.1	HARRIOT] italic small caps
85.4	see, the] see ,the
92.23	prejudiced] prejuced
103.1	I FEEL] italic small caps
105.12	FROM] From
106.8	HARRIOT] italic small caps
107.18	*Fawcet;*] *Fawcet;*
109.2	"Moderate] _∧Moderate
109.5	misfortunes."] misfortunes._∧
110.14	mother._∧] mother."
111.10	*days:*] *days:*
114.3	*Harrington:*] *Harrington:*
126.7	*accessary;*] *accessary;*
141.12	HARRIOT] italic small caps
153.23	rapture] rupture
155.3	HARRIOT] italic small caps
162.2	easier] casier
178.15	Guardian] Gaurdian
178.22	hers] her's
179.8	*Harrington;*] *Harrington;*
181.17	guardian] gaurdian

VARIANTS
IN THE FIRST EDITION

THE VARIANTS listed here were discovered in the course of collating the following ten copies of the first edition: Boston Athenaeum (A), Barrett Collection (University of Virginia) presentation copy (B1), Barrett copy with unsigned frontispiece (B2), uncut Barrett copy (B3), Newberry Library (C), Henry E. Huntington Library (H), the editor's collection (K), Library of Congress (L), New York Public Library (N), and Mrs. Robert C. Taylor Collection (University of Virginia) (T). Each entry gives the page and line reference in the first edition, the variant readings, and the symbols for copies in which the respective readings are found.

I.42.12

as much as any body]   A, B1, B3, C, H, K, L, N, T
∧ much as any body]   B2

I.65.signature

E2]   B3
F2]   A, B1, B2, C, H, K, L, N, T

I.97.4

glos-]   A, B1, B2, C, T
glos∧]   B3, H, K, L, N

I.99.3

OPHELIA] B2, H, K, L, N
italic small caps] A, B1, B3, C, T

I.100.catchword

OPHELIA] B1
italic small caps] A, B2, B3, C, H, K, L, N, T

I.101.1

OPHELIA] H, K, L, N
italic small caps] A, B1, B2, B3, C, T

II.21.6

weigh little in] B1, B3, L
weigh ∧ in] A, B2, C, H, K, N, T

II.119.1

spirits] A, B2, C, H, L, N, T
spi rits] B1, B3, K

II.119.7

we shall find] A, B2, C, H, L, N, T
we sh all find] B1, B3, K

II.125.11

g in preparing elevated] B1
g in preparing normal] L
g in preparing partially depressed] A, C, H, K, N, T
g in preparing depressed] B2, B3

II.149.7

few] N
∧ew] A, B1, B2, B3, C, H, K, L, T

II.149.10

gentleman] A, B1, B2, C, H, L, N, T
gentlema∧] B3, K

[198]

II.150.heading

LETTER] A, N
ETT ER] B1
ET TER] B2
E TTER] B3, C
ETTER] H, K, T
E TT ER] L

II.150.9

duty---but (first hyphen partially present)]
                    A, B1, K, L, N, T

duty --but] B2, B3, C, H

COLLATION OF THE
MASSACHUSETTS MAGAZINE
PASSAGES

THE FIRST number of Isaiah Thomas's *Massachusetts Magazine*, that for January, 1789, contained the following letter:

To the EDITORS *of the* MASSACHUSETTS MAGAZINE.

GENTLEMEN,

I do myself the pleasure to send you the following Extracts from the "First AMERICAN NOVEL," *which I hope you will insert in your first Magazine. I am your Friend and Subscriber,* CALISTA.

Following this letter, on pp. 50–53, eleven passages from the novel were printed under the heading: BEAUTIES of "The POWER of SYMPATHY." Listed below are all of the textual variants, apart from matters of styling, between the first edition and the magazine version of these selections. Given first are the first edition page and line references and the first edition readings, followed by the readings in the magazine. The headings used for the magazine selections are followed by page and line references to these passages in the present text.

BEAUTY. (17.24–18.4)

I.24.17 despise—] despise;
I.25.2 triumph—It] triumph. [End of excerpt.]

NOVELS. (28.11–28.19)

I.42.2   praiseworthy.—Novels] praiseworthy.∧Novels

FEMALE STUDY. (31.19–33.8)

I.48.1   observed,∧] observed,"
I.48.2   ∧in] "in
I.48.10   penetrating—the] penetrating, the
I.48.11   tawdry—what] tawdry, what
I.48.15   "IN] ∧In
I.49.4   when, perhaps,] when∧ perhaps∧
I.49.9   "A YOUNG] ∧A young
I.50.3   *Whitman*] *Whitman*∧
I.51.7   heart∧] heart,

SELF KNOWLEDGE. (40.14–40.24)

No variants.

SELF COMPLACENCY. (94.17–94.23)

No variants.

SENSIBILITY. (104.25–105.17)

II.33.9   way-worn] way∧worn

TEARS. (120.14–120.23)

II.59.17 "BLESSED] ∧Blessed
II.60.8   dammed] damned

INGRATITUDE. (158.24–159.8)

II.122.9 surprize] surprise
II.123.1 heaven] Heaven

SUICIDE. (165.7–166.8)

II.133.17 riveted] rivet-|ted
II.134.1 Our] our

CONSCIENCE. (122.23–123.16)

II.64.1   "FROM] ∧From

SEDUCTION. (116.9–118.6)

II.53.1   "BEHOLD] ⋀Behold
II.53.13   intentions—] intentions,
II.54.1   "o!] ⋀O!
II.54.5   "is] ⋀Is
II.54.16   a life,] a a life,
II.54.17   possessour,] possessor,
II.55.1   "BEHOLD] ⋀Behold
II.55.8   "SUCH] ⋀Such
II.56.3   asunder.——I am, &c.] asunder.⋀

[End of excerpt.]

WORD-DIVISION

THE FOLLOWING compounds and possible compounds are hyphenated at the end of a line in the present text; in the first edition all were printed as one word.

17.19–20	allconquering
19.26–27	wherewith
27.22–23	overlooked
48.7–8	loadstone
57.8–9	midnight
89.21–22	nobleman
94.6–7	*transatlantick*
95.26–27	countrywomen
134.2–3	offspring
151.4–5	præexistant
153.12–13	extraordinary
165.13–14	sunshine
167.15–16	offspring
175.8–9	midnight
180.4–5	overwhelmed

The following compounds and possible compounds, hyphenated at the end of a line in the first edition, are

printed within a line in the present text in the form
given here.

9.5	earth-born
25.19	today
34.25	*Watertown*
51.5	faint-hearted
60.16	brother-in-law
101.1	wiseacres
125.6	forever
177.13	overtake